MODERN STYLE
A CATALOGUE OF CONTEMPORARY DESIGN

Overleaf: Stained glass panels by Shelley Jurs for the main entryway, Larkspur Library, Larkspur, California.

MODERN STYLE
A CATALOGUE OF CONTEMPORARY DESIGN

Compiled by Lawrence Grow
Carl Zimmer, General Editor

THE MAIN STREET PRESS • PITTSTOWN, NEW JERSEY

First edition 1985

Copyright © 1985 by The Main Street Press

Published by
The Main Street Press, Inc.
William Case House
Pittstown, NJ 08867

Published simultaneously in Canada by
Methuen Publications
2330 Midland Avenue
Agincourt, Ontario M1S 1P7

Printed in the United States of America

Library of Congress Cataloging in Publication Data

Grow, Lawrence.
  Modern Style.

  Bibliography: p. 219.
  Includes index.
  1. Interior decoration—History—20th century—
Themes, motives. I. Zimmer, Carl. II. Title.
NK1980.G76 1985   747.2'049   85-19794
ISBN 0-915590-85-9
ISBN 0-915590-83-2 (pbk.)

Contents

Intro-
duction

Modern Style is about the best designers and makers of contemporary furnishings for the home. These are individuals whose work is dedicated to quality and innovation. Some are imaginative craftsmen, and many of the one-of-a-kind objects they have created are presented here for the first time. Other designers are better known. These include such famous names as Donghia, Graves, Aalto, Breuer, and Knoll—household words in the world of interior design. Their modern designs are classics of home furnishings.

Arranged in six chapters devoted to architectural elements, lighting, kitchens and baths, decorative finishes, furniture, and decorative accessories, Modern Style explores every facet of interior design. There are over 500 entries and as many illustrations in black and white and color which provide essential information on the newest and most appropriate products and services useful in the designing, furnishing, or remodeling of a contemporary interior. Modern Style is, simply, a portable decorator, available whenever you wish to consult it, and eminently affordable.

The modern style can take many forms—the flowing horizontal lines of Frank Lloyd Wright architecture and furniture, the square formalism of Mies van der Rohe and his Bauhaus followers, the curving shapes of 1930s Art Deco, the high-tech structuralism of the '70s, and the neo-classically inspired designs of those who now call themselves postmoderns. The many objects and designs exhibited in Modern Style illustrate the unusual amount of freedom and originality of expression found today in the world of contemporary design. There is simply no "right" style but, rather, alternative approaches to contemporary fashion.

Contemporary fashions in furnishings are often presented in such a glossy manner that they appear to be beyond economic reach. The cost of the objects and services presented in Modern Style are, on the average, no more expensive than mundane objects without any style or flair. Even when remodeling a kitchen or bath—two of the most costly areas of the house to outfit—it can pay to use something of higher quality than standard cabinets and appliances. And there are well-designed mass-produced products for even these rooms. Colorful and durable hardware, for instance, can brighten an otherwise dull and uninteresting bath; inexpensive basket storage units will provide convenient, portable space for small kitchen appliances and utensils.

Almost all of the objects and services offered in Modern Style can be purchased directly from the supplier or through one of its retail outlets, the addresses of which will be provided upon request by the supplier. The few special items limited to the interior design trade can be found in the decorating departments of selected department stores. Again, these names will be supplied upon request by the manufacturer.

Whether as a practical guide to buying the best in contemporary furnishings and design services or as a welcome sourcebook of ideas for the future, *Modern Style* will serve to provoke discussion, to widen the choices available to everyone who appreciates fine modern design, and to promote the work of the most able contemporary craftsmen and manufacturers.

The task of compiling a complex sourcebook requires the skills of an enterprising and dedicated staff. Carl Zimmer, general editor, brought the contents together with an eye to originality and practicality. Liz Rolfe provided the organizational brains behind the scene, gathering and organizing the source material. And Martin Greif, managing editor, brought everything together into proper editorial focus. The handsome design of *Modern Style* is owed to the special efforts of art director Frank Mahood and his assistants John Fox and Lisa Magaz. To all these persons I owe my very sincere thanks.

Lawrence Grow
Pittstown, New Jersey

MODERN STYLE

A CATALOGUE OF CONTEMPORARY DESIGN

1.

Architectural Elements

Buildings of distinctive contemporary design are becoming more and more popular. While a majority of North Americans still prefer a traditional home outfitted with some modern touches, a new generation of builders and homeowners enthusiastically endorses such hallmarks of contemporary architecture as an open floor plan, dramatic use of glass and exposed structural members, and multilevel living space. The center-hall Georgian Colonial with attached garage is not yet an endangered species, but its days may be numbered. The same trend toward contemporary design is even more marked in apartment and condominium construction.

The architectural elements used to define a contemporary space should be similar in expression to the structure itself. Windows, flooring, stairways, trim, hardware—all of these elements deserve careful consideration. They should complement the overall space in proportion and material content. Within these guidelines, however, an enormous range of choices remains to be made. Since the modern style has evolved dramatically in recent years from the cold formality of the Bauhaus school, such diverse elements as stained glass panels, architectural ornaments, and spiral stair systems are among the imaginative options to be considered.

One of the special features of many contemporary homes is a greenhouse—or a sunspace, as this room is often called today. A sunspace can be incorporated in the main structure or added on. It takes full advantage of the architectural possibilities of the modern style and dramatically opens a home or apartment to the outdoors in a protected and therefore useful manner.

Flooring, decorative trim, glass, windows and doors, stair systems, and hardware are correctly termed architectural elements. All to some degree are basic to the proper fitting out of the structure. To these essentials may be added extras such as sunspaces and fireplaces. In designing a new house or remodeling an old one, a great deal of mixing and matching will take place. The ultimate test of the final arrangement will be the degree of harmony that it achieves.

Two-story addition, Mayer townhouse, New York City, designed by Duo Dickinson, Louis Mackall & Partner, Architects, Branford, Connecticut.

Flooring Materials

Floors are not usually a matter of major concern when a home is being built or remodeled. But they should be, especially in this day and age when what is underfoot is often only a slab of concrete and, instead of wood, tile, or stone, a thin shaving of synthetic carpeting. A well-designed contemporary home or apartment deserves something much better. A handsome floor sets the stage for the act to follow. There are thousands of types of designs and materials to examine when selecting flooring and, as in other areas of design, choices may be difficult to make. The following write-ups serve as an introduction to some of the best materials to be considered.

AMARU TILES

The handsome European designs imported by Amaru invigorate the whole field of ceramic tile flooring. Amaru tiles from Italy are made in large-sized pieces for effective use in large "open-plan" interiors. Almost all floor tiles are available in 12"-square or 12" by 16" dimensions. The Fratello Sorella tiles with a soft criss-cross pattern in six different shades (rose, gray, oxford, beige, brown, and khaki) are made in 16" squares. Linea I Consoli is a line of slim 2¼" by 10" and 5" by 10" tiles in white, gold, black, platinum, cream, beige, blue, red, or gray. Linea Sheraton is a series of tiles with optical design effects in 8"-square blocks and a color selection of white, black, gray, platinum, gold, cream, and red.

For further information, contact:

*Amaru Tile
D & D Building,
979 Third Ave.
New York, NY 10022
(212) 750-8804*

GMT/eden

Vinyl floor covering has changed greatly since its introduction over thirty years ago. The material has improved in durability and design. GMT/eden is one of the most enterprising manufacturers of vinyl flooring. Illustrated are two of its newest products: a series of marbleized patterns available in a variety of colors and

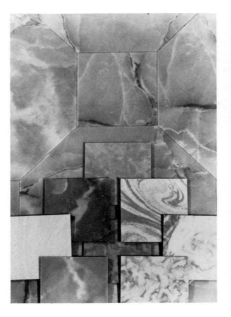

sizes, and Le Clay, a natural-appearing quarry tile design offered in ten shades and standard sizes.

For further information, contact:

*GMT Associates
1255 Oak Point Ave.
Bronx, NY 10474
(212) 991-8500*

AMERICAN OLEAN TILE

As one of the major North American suppliers of ceramic tile, American Olean offers an astonishing array of products, most of which can be found in local outlets. The more commonly used flooring tiles are available in 4½" and 6" squares, and 4½" and 5" hexagons. Less well known are such tiles as Quarry Mesa, a 6" burnt-orange square with the look of handcrafted tile. The Elegance line of 12"-square marble tiles is manufactured in Italy for American Olean. Ten colors ranging from Carrara white to deep green-black Nero are available.

For further information, contact:

*American Olean Tile Co.
1000 Cannon Ave., P.O. Box 271
Lansdale, PA 19446
(215) 855-1111*

NATURAL VINYL FLOOR

Solid vinyl tiles have a durability that recommends them above all other synthetic flooring materials. Colors and patterns resist scuffing and fading. Natural Vinyl manufactures a basic line of solid-color 12"-square tiles in ⅛" thickness. The range of 27 colors is very pleasing, and two or three shades can be combined with dramatic effect.

The Real Wood Collection is somewhat of a misnomer, but there is no mistaking the durability of this wood-clad series of tiles. They combine the best of solid vinyl materials with as natural a substance as can be found. Each tile consists of a ⅛"-thick sandwich of pure transparent vinyl, wood, and pure opaque vinyl. Walnut, red oak, ash, cherry, teak, pecan, mozambique, and mahogany-finish tiles are featured in various sizes.

For further information, contact:

Natural Vinyl Floor Co.
4401 Mars Hill Rd.
P.O. Box 1302
Florence, AL 35631
(800) 633-3380
In Alabama (800) 942-3109

STARBUCK GOLDNER STUDIOS

Flat handmade ceramic tile of high quality and imaginative design is the forte of Steven Goldner and Beth Starbuck. They work by commission only, producing pieces that can be brought together in unique designs. Pinwheel Pentagons is the name of the floor pattern of unglazed flat tiles illustrated here. Such smooth-surfaced tiles can also be used for counters, tables, and stove and fireplace surrounds. Goldner and Starbuck also design and fabricate decorative relief tiles. For further information regarding designs suitable for walls, see the listing for the studio in the Decorative Finishes chapter.

Brochure available.

Starbuck Goldner Studios
315 W. 4th St.
Bethlehem, PA 18015
(215) 866-6321

TARKETT

Postmodern ideas have entered the flooring world in the medium of vinyl tiling. Expressions is the name of Tarkett's line of new architectural tiles of soft coloration, muted shades popularly used by today's design trend setters. Brush beige, painter's green, palette blue, master's mauve, graphite gray, gallery gray, canvas tan, and artist's almond are the color names used by the manufacturer. Each color group of 12"-square tiles is available with a coordinated 1"-wide accent strip and cove base pieces. Introduced for commercial use, the Expressions tiles are just as suitable for residential purposes.

For further information, contact:

Tarkett Inc.
P.O. Box 264
Parsippany, NJ 07054
(201) 428-9000

VERMONT FLOORS & PANELING

Solid wood floors are as attractive in contemporary homes as they are in traditional settings. The fundamental honesty of such quality hardwoods as ash, oak, cherry, birch, and butternut—all offered by Vermont—constitutes much of the aesthetic appeal. Whether highly polished or scrubbed down to a soft finish, such floors provide an attractive and natural stage for the display of modern furnishings. Vermont Floors & Paneling prides itself on providing yesterday's quality today. The firm's flooring—untouched by polyurethane or other coatings—is available in random lengths from 6' to 12' and 3", 4", and 5" face-width measures. All Vermont Flooring is ¾"-thick solid wood with tongue-and-groove edges and unsquared ends.

For further information, contact:

Vermont Floors & Paneling
683 Pine St.
Burlington, VT 05401
(802) 658-5670

VERMONT MARBLE

If there is a choice to be made between stone and less durable flooring for an entry hall, bath, or kitchen, most people would choose the finer material. Since cost determines what can be used in almost all homes, marble, slate, and brownstone are usually out of the picture. A careful comparison of costs, however, discloses that these materials are not that much more expensive than ceramic tile or solid vinyl flooring—two quality alternatives. Marble, as they say, endures forever. Fine quality marble is available in polished or satin-finish ⅜"-thick squares from Vermont Marble and is made in three standard sizes: 12" square, 12" by 5⅞", and 5⅞" square. Colors range from snowy white to black.

Another stone available from Vermont—brownstone—is illustrated here. It is a soft russet color and is manufactured in the same sizes as marble.

For further information, contact:

Vermont Marble Co.
61 Main St.
Proctor, VT 05765
(802) 459-3311

Architectural Ornamentation

The square boxes which pass for modern living spaces in most post-World War II homes and apartments supply little imagination for everyday life. Plump pillows and copies of Ar-chitectural Digest or Metropolitan

Home may introduce some color and hope for the future, but little sub-stance. It needn't be this way. There are hundreds of ways to bring the lines of even the most banal interiors to life. Moldings, architectural antiques,

painted designs, carved panels, ceramic tile, an innovative fireplace— these options and others are explored in the following pages. The entries are arranged by firm or craftsman.

Mike Hales

LOUIS MACKALL & PARTNER

A good architectural design firm can undertake everything from minor im-provements to a kitchen or bath to the addition of rooms. The Mackall part-nership is better equipped than many firms to provide complete remodeling services as it includes a woodworking division, Breakfast Woodworks. In tandem, the design and production teams have successfully completed many residential projects of an un-usual character. The design aesthetic of the firm can be loosely described as postmodern, the adaptation of classically inspired forms to modern settings. Unlike many practitioners of this faddish style, however, the prin-cipals of the Mackall firm do not sacrifice the principles of proportion to fancy or substitute the standards of quality for pure effect.

A project involving a two-story addition to a New York City townhouse is il-lustrated here and as the frontispiece to this chapter. The lower level of the addition comprises a breakfast nook. The second floor is living space used principally for entertaining. Above it, a deck has been added off the master bedroom. This design by Duo Dickin-son serves as counterpoint to the flat regularity of the townhouse's original façade. The windows, although cus-tom fabricated, are of aluminum and much less expensive than wood counterparts.

The interior fireplace design by Mackall & Partner illustrates the firm's approach to conventional architectural elements. This is not merely a heating unit, but a piece of sculpture as well. An inexpensive prefabricated firebox has been integrated with a standard frame and dry wall box. The frame is made of cherry and padauk; the un-

usual millwork mantel, of solid walnut; mahogany veneer is used at the bottom.

For further information regarding Louis Mackall & Partner, contact:

Louis Mackall & Partner
50 Maple St.
Branford, CT 06405
(203) 488-8364

TROMPLOY

When structural work such as creating new windows is out of the question because of cost or space limitations, a decorative treatment may be the best alternative. Many of today's decorative painters are well trained to provide the illusion of space where none exists. The partners in Tromploy, Gary Finkel and Clyde Wachsberger, created a view of Central Park where it should be but isn't—at the end of a New York City apartment hall. Many apartments —whether in the city or outside—have need of an opening to the outer world.

Prisoners of modern space too often take for granted that they are boxed in forever.

For another example of Tromploy's inventive work, see the listing in the chapter on Kitchens and Bathrooms.

Additional information is available by contacting:

Tromploy Studio and Gallery
400 Lafayette St., 5th Floor
New York, NY 10003
(212) 420-1639

CREATIVE ADDITIONS

The architectural definition supplied by traditional moldings has been neglected until recently in contemporary interiors. While elaborate bands of deep-relief trim are still not called for in a modern setting, some ornamental touches are gaining favor. The Bright Lines collection of metallic strips from Creative Additions offers convenient, straightforward alternatives in brass and chrome to traditional moldings. The strips may be used to define wall panels, doors and windows, and to set off walls from ceiling. Bright lines are either flat or gently curved and are without any decoration or relief design. They are available in half-round and flat profiles. Pliable enough to wrap around a 90° corner, they range in widths from 1/4" to 1".

For further information, contact:

Creative Additions Ltd.
134 W. 26th St.
New York, NY 10001
(212) 679-1515

DECORATORS SUPPLY

For several generations architects and interior designers have turned to Decorators Supply for wood fiber, composition, and cast-plaster decorations. Such elements as cornices, pilasters, shells, brackets, and capitals find their greatest use in period buildings. Increasingly, however, they are finding their way into what is now termed the postmodern interior. Pilasters and columns are among the favorite motifs being employed today in fashionable residential settings. Decorators Supply can provide you with catalogues displaying its various offerings. Among the most useful of these publications are:

Catalogue #124, 350 pages, covering the complete line of 13,000 patterns of composition carvings; available for $15.

Catalogue #130, 60 pages, illustrating the line of cast ornamental plaster work; $3.

Catalogue #127, 44 pages, illustrating the complete line of column capitals and brackets; $3.

The catalogues are sent on approval when remittance is sent. The cost will be refunded if they are returned in 60 days.

FOCAL POINT

Focal Point is the leading supplier of traditional architectural ornaments made of modern polymer materials. This substance—Endure-all—is easy to use and has the advantage over plasterwork of being considerably less expensive. Joining pieces of molding and working around corners requires skill, but not the expert assistance of a professional. The simple cove molding illustrated here has a sculptural line suitable for use in 1920s and '30s modern interiors. The height of the piece is 6⅜" and the profile angles out the same distance. The molding can be purchased in various lengths and is pre-primed in beige for final staining or in white for painting. In addition to Endure-all, supplied in approximately 10-foot lengths, Focal Point can supply an even more flexible material, Contour-all, which is especially useful in round or oval spaces.

For further information, contact:

Focal Point, Inc.
2005 Marietta Rd., NW
Atlanta, GA 30318
(404) 351-0820

For further information, contact:

The Decorators Supply Corp.
3610-3612 S. Morgan St., No. 26
Chicago, IL 60609
(312) 847-6300

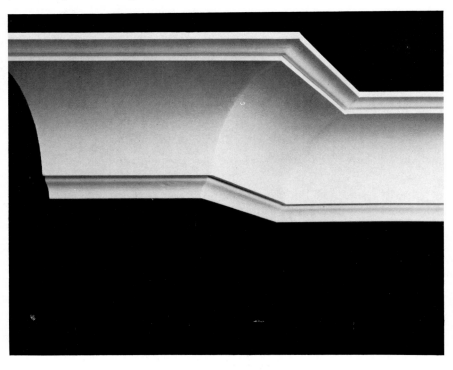

doors or used in space dividers. All of Jane Goco's work, of course, is one-of-a-kind, and is undertaken by commission only.

For further information, contact:

Jane Goco
794 Scott Rd., Box 88
Lewisville, NC 27023
(919) 945-3851

IRREPLACEABLE ARTIFACTS

Using salvage architectural ornamentation in modern settings has become something of a fad. Bits and pieces thrown together in a gratuitous manner add up to nothing, but well-chosen and imaginatively placed objects may bring a dull space alive. Irreplaceable Artifacts can accomplish the latter. It is one of the largest suppliers of salvage pieces—including friezes, plaques, Art Deco railings, and elevator doors. The business has grown so rapidly that there are now three Manhattan locations:

Irreplaceable Artifacts
1046 Third Ave.
New York, NY 10021
(212) 223-4411

Irreplaceable Artifacts (showroom
*   and office)*
14 Second Ave.
New York, NY 10003
(212) 777-2900

Irreplaceable Artifacts (warehouse
*   outlet)*
259 Bowery
New York, NY 10003
(212) 982-5000

JANE GOCO

Jane Goco is a gifted wood sculptor specializing in architectural panels which add interest and beauty to an interior. Illustrated is a relief panel of Honduras mahogany, 95" by 53", entitled Tamaraw Falls: Orchid Jungle. Decorative panels such as this example may be incorporated in interior

ENTASIS

Entasis deals freely in deception. Offering various forms of architectural painting such as faux marbre and trompe l'oeil, the Maryland firm can decorate walls with imaginative illusions or impressive imitations that delight the eye. Shown here is Eugene Perreau's faux marbre treatment of an office wall with latex paint. Not only is it beautiful in its combination of soft colors and its amazing

mimicry of tiles, but it is less expensive than the real thing. The process of putting up marble tile is long and costly—one must prepare the wall and cut pieces of marble to fit along borders, for example. Using several different colors of marble makes the undertaking even more costly. And if you later have to take the tiles off, you practically need explosives to do so. Painting, on the other hand, requires

little wall preparation, and Entasis can decorate walls with colors in which marble never existed.

For further information about the firm's architectural painting, contact:

Entasis
5301 Westbard Circle
Bethesda, MD 20816
(703) 525-8478

Jim Burtnett

Derrick & Love

MARAZZI CERAMIC TILE

Tiles are almost always considered suitable only for kitchens and baths, but their utility and beauty recommend them for other settings. Here tiles are used most effectively for a fireplace surround, apron, and side console. 12½" by 12½" Metropoli tiles from Marazzi in the Londra color are employed in a private Harrington Park, N.J., residence designed by Eric Bernard. Marazzi, one of the world's largest ceramic tile manufacturers, offers a wide range of glazed and unglazed single-fired tiles of high quality.

For further information, contact:

Marazzi USA, Inc.
55 Clay and Scyene Rd.
Sunnyvale, TX 75182
(214) 226-0110

Architectural Glass

Of all essential building materials, glass is the most versatile. It can be formed and finished in thousands of different ways to create unusual effects. The ordinary need for window glass is easily filled by suppliers found in every area. Special types of glass, however, require some searching out. Fortunately, there are many studios and craftsmen who produce imaginative designs which will enhance any interior. Opaque or stained glass panels, for example, can be used as bathroom windows. Sand-blasted or etched panels are suitable for interior and exterior doors.

ED CARPENTER

Carpenter is an undisputed master of architectural glass design. His commissions include numerous residences in the Northwest and important public buildings, including the Justice Center in Portland, Oregon, seen in the illustration. Thoroughly trained in the United States, England, and Germany in the art of stained glass design and fabrication, he has won award after award. Carpenter is particularly skilled in translating architectural forms in glass, in designing windows that perfectly suit the building in which they are used. "I try to make the window look as if it was hatched from the same egg as the building," he explains.

The massive window designed for the Justice Center makes use of German, American, and French hand-blown glass. Mirrored, transparent, and translucent panes change in color and intensity with the light. The actual fabrication of all Carpenter's designs is executed by craftsman Tim O'Neill, with whom Carpenter has worked for a number of years.

For further information, contact:

Ed Carpenter
1812 N.W. 24th Ave.
Portland, OR 97210
(503) 224-6729

Karlis Grants

FORMS & SURFACES

Glass block was widely used in the 1930s to great effect, but then faded away in popularity. Designers of the '80s have brought it back again for good reason—it can provide privacy, a filtered medium of light, and is architecturally interesting. Pittsburgh Corning Glass makes glass block available in nearly every part of the continent; Forms & Surfaces does, too, and offers an even greater selection of attractive forms.

Illustrated are several of Forms & Surfaces' more unusual types of glass block: Fantasy, available in 8″ and 12″ squares, in which the glass is slightly crazed to provide discontinuous images; Circlet, offered in 5″ squares, with a ring pressed into the center;

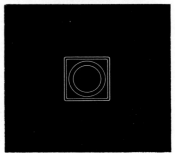

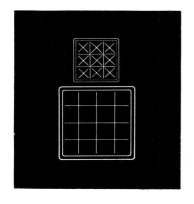

and Glass Pavers, made either as an 8″-square matrix or 5″-square prism, designed for use in floors or ceilings.

All of Forms & Surfaces' patterns are available with a color rim rather than a standard white rim. Colors are sky blue, blue, mossy-green, green, orange, yellow, brown, and gray.

For further information, contact:

Forms & Surfaces
Box 5215
Santa Barbara, CA 93108
(805) 969-7721

JURS ARCHITECTURAL GLASS

Shelley Jurs brings the medium of glass alive in the most imaginative ways. Her design for panels lining the main entryway of the Larkspur Library, Larkspur, California, featured as the

frontispiece to this book, capture the full aesthetic potential of glass. The panels, while frozen in place, reflect, transmit, and refract the ever-changing scene. With a multitude of surfaces, colors, and shapes, each panel catches the eye as light plays optical tricks.

For further information about Jurs's work, contact:

Jurs Architectural Glass
1681 8th St.
Oakland, CA 94607
(415) 763-6796

MICHAEL KENNEDY STUDIOS

Michael Kennedy, founder and chief designer of the firm bearing his name, is in the avant-garde of stained glass design. His work is thoroughly contemporary, being postmodern in expression. Work such as that illustrated here takes full advantage of the painterly qualities of stained glass. Form builds on form like a puzzle for which only the artist has the solution. Kennedy's residential commissions are somewhat more architectural than

the example shown and feature such motifs as interwoven ribbons of color and geometric structures.

For further information about the designer's work, contact:

Michael Kennedy Studios
1927 7th Ave.
Seattle, WA 98101
(206) 441-3737

MARNI BAKST

Marni Bakst's stained glass designs are now well known in modern architectural circles. She has executed commercial and residential commissions in the New York area. And her work has not suffered one bit because of such acceptance. She is an expert interpreter of light and color in the medium of opaque glass. Lead is used not simply to hold the pieces of a composition, but to emphasize line. The panels she designs are forceful and lively, overflowing with movement.

Illustrated in color is a panel designed for Le Delice restaurant in Whippany, New Jersey. Would that all dining establishments were blessed with such fine art. Seen in black and white is a dining room window made for a New York City residence.

For further information regarding her work, contact the artist directly:

Marni Bakst Glass Design
235 E. 5th St. #2
New York, NY 10003
(212) 533-2556

PETER MOLLICA

Mollica has chosen to tread a special path, that of providing stained glass windows and panels for bathrooms. This is not to say that his handsome designs cannot be used effectively in other areas of the house such as a front hall or study. They can be, but, because bathrooms require privacy, stained glass can serve an especially useful function. Mollica has explained his own interest particularly well:

Charles Frizzell

"Sometimes a bathroom can be a well-appointed and well-designed space in which stained glass can be an integral part of the concept . . . Just as often, however, stained glass is required for privacy or to give some spark of life to a tiny closet-like bathroom. . . . I enjoy both these challenges. The chance to be part of a well thought-out space—to be in effect, the radiator grill on a Rolls-Royce is a delight. But it is also fun to be one of those Rolls Royce grills you sometimes see retrofitted into a Volkswagen."

For further information, contact:

Peter Mollica
10033 Broadway Terr.
Oakland, CA 94611
(415) 655-5736

BEVERLY REISER

Architectural glass of several varieties is imaginatively designed and fabricated by this leading California artist. Leaded stained glass windows are basic ingredients in her portfolio, but of even greater interest are such compositions as that illustrated—Neon Spring—worked in neon light and sandblasted mirror glass. Panels such as these can be used as windows, wall-hangings, skylights, and in many other ways.

For further information, contact:

Beverly Reiser
6979 Exeter Dr.
Oakland, CA 94611
(415) 482-2483

JAMES B. FURMAN

Jim Furman's work is rigorously architectural but remains innovative in feeling. His designs, reminiscent of the best examples of the early 20th century modern expression, have a discipline and balance missing from the work of less practiced stained glass artists. "I work in a style that often features special surface treatment," Furman says. "This might include the use of laminations in metal or glass, sandblasting, or painting. I sometimes juxtapose hand-blown glass with machine-made or patterned mechanical glass." The panels illustrated here incorporate the use of several types of glass and techniques in handling them.

For further information, contact:

James B. Furman Glass Studio
27 W. Main St.
Trumansburg, NY 14886
(607) 387-4141

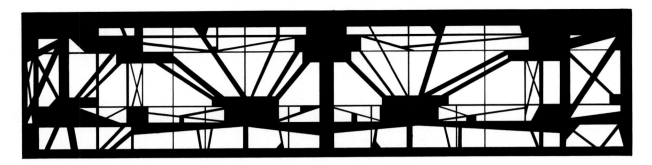

SHEILA RITZ

The structural designs in glass and lead came executed by Sheila Ritz are refreshingly innovative. She uses the joining element of lead as imaginatively as glass to compose her panels. Each commission she undertakes is unique, but all share a great love of taut line and geometric form. Trained in England and New York City, she lives in Brooklyn, the borough that gave us the wonderful suspension bridge that has inspired so many artists. Her artwork suggests that she must work near its span.

Slides and a resumé are available upon request.

Sheila Ritz
149-151 Grand St.
Brooklyn, NY 11211
(718) 387-3286

Architectural Screens

The use of screens to hide an unsightly view, to provide privacy in a large room, or to cut down on wintry drafts was once very common. Today screens have been rediscovered and are valued for their utility and aesthetic value. Architectural screens are sometimes called moveable walls. They have a special usefulness in a modern open-plan home or apartment.

DIANA ARCADIPONE

One-of-a-kind folding shoji screens are designed and fabricated by Diana Arcadipone in her Boston workshop. The wood frames are carved by hand and the paper is handmade as well. A special blend of cotton, flax, and abaca fiber is used and decorated with painted images while the material is still wet. The paper has a neutral pH factor and is thus destined to last for many years to come.

For further information, contact:

Diana Arcadipone
5 Goodwin Pl., #3
Boston, MA 02114
(617) 338-2173

LIZA LAMB DESIGNS

Screens provide a simple means to hide a dull wall or to partition a room. Liza Lamb covers her screens with ikat fabric (dyed before weaving) that can be color coordinated to suit various room designs. The four 72″ by 18″ wooden panels are tall enough to

Courtney Frisse

highlight the verticality of the attractive bands of color on the cotton fabrics.

For further information, contact:

Liza Lamb Designs
533 Glenwood Rd.
Binghamton, NY 13905
(607) 770-0159

RICK WRIGLEY FURNITURE

Cabinetmaker Rick Wrigley has collaborated with artist Catherine Creamer on a series of architectural screens of unusual quality. Wrigley is responsible for the cherry frames; and Creamer, the hand-woven and dyed 100%-silk panels. The model illustrated here is 72″ tall by 72″ wide by 1¼″ deep. The frame is finished in a clear lacquer.

The screens are available directly from Wrigley or through a New York gallery.

Allen Bragdon

For further information, contact:

Rick Wrigley
80 Race St.
Holyoke, MA 01040
(413) 536-2034

or

ZONA
484 Broome St.
New York, NY 10013
(212) 925-6750

Architectural Hardware

Unlike the traditional home, a contemporary residence does not make noticeable use of architectural hardware. What is visible is simply what is needed—functional, durable knobs, locks, and pulls. Consequently, there is little demand for specially designed pieces. All the major hardware manufacturers, however, do carry designs with modern lines. Special suppliers of bath and kitchen hardware are included in Chapter 3.

FORMS & SURFACES

Architectural hardware produced by this California-based building materials firm is of exceptional design and quality. The knob sets are from the Omni Hardware Group, Marchesi Series. Illustrated are the wood line with metal parts in a polished brass finish. Each knob set includes two knobs, two roses, and an appropriate spindle; the set is used with a latch set available from Forms & Surfaces or it can be fitted to any major U.S.-manufactured mortise lock set.

The door pulls are from the Modern Classics Series designed by Sherrill Broudy, Architect. They are cast in bronze, brass, or aluminum, and have a hand-rubbed natural finish.

For further information, contact:

Forms & Surfaces
Hardware Division
Box 5215
Santa Barbara, CA 93108
(805) 969-7721

Sunspaces

Despite suggestions to the contrary from Washington, solar heating — active or passive — is not a thing of the past. In fact, even Yuppies love the design of sunspaces and appreciate their utility. Anyone remodeling or building a contemporary home would be foolish not to consider the incorporation of such a space. Many of the problems first apparent in greenhouse or sunroom designs — lack of proper insulation, inadequate ventilation — have been satisfactorily resolved. The pleasure of outdoors can be brought indoors in a contemporary home, thanks to advances in technology.

Frank Armstrong

DECK HOUSE

Since 1960 Deck House has been an important supplier of contemporary home designs and construction packages. The New England-based company is noted for its post and beam construction system, high-quality building materials, and functional design sense. Since 1980, and the introduction of the company's first Conservatory House, a reputation for passive solar dwellings has grown rapidly. Today, more than half of all the 6,000-plus Deck Houses in the United States are of the Conservatory variety with either a built-in or added sunspace.

Illustrated is one of the most popular and practical Conservatory House designs—the two-story, 1,800-square foot Model 7313. The 22' by 24' cathedral-ceiling sunspace serves as a dining area and living room. (Only the living area is visible here.) Overlooking the room on the second floor are two balconies off a master bedroom and hall. The house also contains a kitchen, laundry space, den, lavatory, a second bedroom, two baths, and a sitting area. The attractiveness of the design, however, derives from the totally integrated sunspace which provides light and an airy spaciousness to the entire house.

Conservatory House and Deck House models now make use of Sungate 100 coated glass by PPG Industries for all sliding glass doors and sash windows. The result in efficiency is greater than triple glazing. The savings in heating costs and air-conditioning is considerable.

Many other Conservatory House Models are available in larger sizes and more complex designs.

Design portfolios available, $12.

Deck House
930 Main St.
Acton, MA 01720
(800) 225-5755
In MA: (617) 259-9450

PRINCETON ENERGY GROUP

Princeton Energy Group's precision-engineered 12' by 24' Sunspace is much more than a passive solar unit. It is designed to substantially reduce winter fuel bills while remaining pleasantly habitable in the warmer months of the year. PEG has de-signed many shed-style greenhouses, and began building the Sunspace model in 1980 when the owner of a classic Federal-style house wanted to add a greenhouse/breakfast room that would be compatible with the main dwelling. The design of Sunspace would complement almost any contemporary home.

During cold months, heat from the sun is absorbed by six water storage tubes, visible in the illustration. The solar heat is vented from these units to other areas of the house. In the residence shown, they provide heat for four upstairs bedrooms. During warm months, a curtain system of white woven polyester fabric (used in professional greenhouses) acts as an effective barrier to heat penetration. The same curtaining, of course, is useful to prevent heat loss on cold winter nights or cloudy days. The Sunspace is also equipped with a thermostatically-controlled ventilation fan.

For further information, contact:

Princeton Energy Group
575 Ewing St.
Princeton, NJ 08540
(609) 921-1965

Stair Systems

Stairways can be the dramatic focal point of a home. In a contemporary residence it is often possible to make use of a free-form stair system which is as attractive as it is practical. Even in an older home or apartment which is being renovated, a spiral staircase which takes up little space can be easily inserted between levels.

MYLEN SPIRAL STAIRS

One of the most attractive features of Mylen's spiral stairways is that most are available in kit form ready for assembly. The CS 100 model, illustrated here, is offered in diameters of 3′ 6″ to 8′ 0″ in 6″ increments. The standard treads are of pre-drilled smooth plate or checkered safety plate. The pre-drilled smooth plate will take wood or carpet-covered plywood. There are optional extras to dress up this model or others, including wood spiral handrails, wood treads, and such trim as newel posts, well molding, rail connectors, and oak cap.

All models are shipped knocked down with all necessary hardware and complete instructions.

For further information, contact:

Mylen Industries, Inc.
650 Washington St.
Box 350
Peekskill, NY 10566
(800) 431-2155
(New York State) (212) 585-6767

YORK SPIRAL STAIR

Each of York's three spiral stairways is a true piece of sculpture. Through the use of special laminated dual stringers and handrails, no centerpost is necessary to support the structure.

Two of the models are small-sized, measuring 5′ and 6′ in diameter; the third is 8½′ in diameter. These are available in either a natural finish red oak or Honduras mahogany.

Each York stair system is custom manufactured and is shipped fully assembled except for the handrails and balusters.

For further information, contact:

York Spiral Stair
Rt. 32
North Vassalboro, ME 04962
(207) 872-5558

Other Suppliers of Architectural Elements

Consult List of Suppliers for addresses.

Flooring Materials

ARD Custom Kitchens & Baths
Bruce Hardwood Floors
Elon, Inc.
Forms and Surfaces
Fresh Impressions
Dorothy Hafner
Hastings Tile & Il Bagno Collection
Hoboken Wood Flooring Corp.
Kentile Floors Inc.
Marazzi USA, Inc.
Marble Concepts Inc.
Parma Tile Mosaic & Marble Co.
Potlach Corporation
Puccio/European Marble Inc.
Rising & Nelson Slate Co., Inc.
Taos Clay Products, Inc.
Villeroy & Boch Inc.
Sherle Wagner International
Waterworks
Westchester Marble & Granite, Inc.

Kenneth Lynch & Sons
E.A. Nord Co., Inc.
Plexability
Puccio/European Marble Works
Rising & Nelson Slate Co., Inc.
Robinson Iron Corp.
Structural Slate Co.
Unique Form Originals
Walker & Zanger
Wall • Goldfinger Associates Inc.
The Wrecking Bar

Architectural Ornamentation

Architectural Paneling Inc.
Art Directions
Baluchi Marble Ltd.
Bendix Mouldings, Inc.
Joel Berman Associates Inc.
Carleton V
Classic Moulders
Domus International
Dovetail, Inc.
Fauxstone
Forbes-Monselle Inc.
Forms & Surfaces
Hunter Douglas Inc.
Jade-Intarsia
Kenmore Industries Inc.
Klise Mfg. Co.
Levolor Lorentzen Inc.

Architectural Glass

Architectural Emphasis, Inc.
Morgan Bockius Studios
Cherry Creek Enterprises
Ray King
Pittsburgh Corning Corp.
Rambusch
Rose/Carter, San Francisco
Penelope Starr
Walker & Zanger

Architectural Hardware

The Decorative Hardware Studio
Hettich Corp.

Sunspaces

Sun System Solar Greenhouses

Stair Systems

Architectural Paneling Inc.
Baluchi Marble Ltd.
Puccio/European Marble Works
Rambusch

2.
Lighting

All the interior designing in the world will obviously be wasted on a room if it is in the dark—lighting is a plain necessity to any design. Often, though, consumers do not understand how complicated the process of illuminating a space is. A wall lamp and a torchiere both generally provide ambient lighting, for example, but while the torchiere creates a distributed light, the wall fixture adds direct uplighting as well, which can draw attention to wall decorations. Track lighting and footlights can be used for streaks of white on surfaces or to highlight furniture. In designing a room, one should therefore pay as much respect for light's effects as a painter does.

Not only is the type of light crucial, but the fixture that supplies it is essential as well. A glowing, well-sculptured fixture can be among the most attractive objects in a room. A consumer now has the luxury of choosing from a large assortment of styles, as more and more manufacturers recognize the merits of a handsome fixture.

Lighting fixtures fall roughly into three styles of design in this chapter. The Art Deco influence remains strong in lighting, most likely because lamps still require materials that were the basic components of all Art Deco work. Many of the fixtures presented here, consequently, consist of nostalgically gleaming tiers of glass, long, smooth sheets of brass, or ribbed sections of chrome. Light also complements Art Deco fixtures as it sparkles over their stylistic details.

The tradition of mechanical fixtures whose beauty derives from their purposefulness carries on in the technologically astounding lighting now being made. Using halogen or fluorescent bulbs, lamp manufacturers create streamlined, well-articulated fixtures with amazing brilliance.

Sculptured fixtures are only beginning to regain their popularity as we enter a post-modern era. Discovering the possibilities of more organically artistic lighting, manufacturers and craftsmen are producing fixtures in the forms of sea shells, flowers, vases, and even birds. These designs probably best demonstrate the importance of how a lamp looks, not only how it lights.

Egisto wall fixtures designed by Angelo Mangiarotti for Artemide Inc.

Table and Desk Lamps

The conventional shade-and-base table lamp seems to be making a comeback against the recent influx of typically swan-necked experiments. Of course, in this age of reinterpretation, these lamps have undergone some transformations: the bases have become sharply curved and exotically etched; the shades, in cloth or glass, have stretched out broadly or have curled into sculptured looks. Other older styles, such as those of Frank Lloyd Wright and the Art Deco tradition, continue to be revived, not just as relics of an earlier age, but as vital designs for the 1980s. And, of course, what selection of contemporary table lamps would be complete without wing-shaped, vase-imitating, and gunbarrel innovations, the reminders that even the table lamp is an art form with inexhaustible variations.

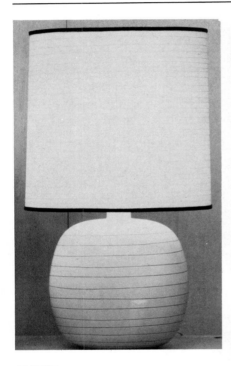

OVONE

The matching off-white stripes of this lamp join the rectangularly cylindrical white linen shade in a sophisticated combination. The shade is 16″ in diameter and the lamp is 31″ high overall. Ovone takes a 250-watt, 3-way light bulb.

For further information, contact:

Koch & Lowy Inc.
21-24 39th Ave.
Long Island City, NY 11101
(718) 786-3520

MODI

Boldly contemporary curves characterize Modi, a line of handmade ceramic lamps from Italy. Available in black, ivory, pink, or yellow bases, these lamps have black or white tissue shantung shades. A high-low switch controls a 150-watt bulb in the shade. The lamp comes in two sizes, 20″ by 25″ and 23″ by 31½″. A similar floor lamp is also available.

For further information, contact:

Nessen Lamps Inc.
621 E. 216th Street
Bronx, NY 10467
(212) 231-0221

MURANO

The four glass creations shown here blur the boundary between illuminated sculptures and table lamps. Made by Murano glass blowers, these cased white glass shapes have in-line switches and come in two sizes in each model. They all accommodate 75-watt bulbs.

Catalogue available, $5.

Illuminating Experiences, Inc.
107 Trumbull St.
Elizabeth, NJ 07206
(201) 527-8847

CONCORDE

The gun-shaped barrel of the Concorde lamp, designed by Hans von Klier, houses a halogen bulb and tilts on its base to provide varying degrees of brightness for task lighting. Both the arm and the base are made of extruded aluminum, capped with high-gloss polycarbonate ends.

For further information, contact:

Innovative Products for Interiors, Inc.
315 E. 62nd St.
New York, NY 10021
(212) 838-2900

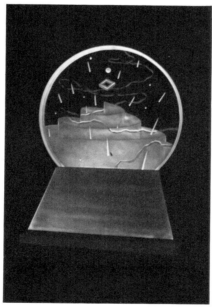

MOON LAMPS

Moon Lamps, designed by Ray King, emanate a lighting effect appropriate to their name, with black and silver optical glass etched with lunar scenes. The base is made of slate and bronze, and the bulb housed in the fixture is touch-switch activated. Moon Lamps measure 17″ high, 13¼″ wide, and 6″ deep.

For more information, contact:

Ray King
603 S. 10th St.
Philadelphia, PA 19147
(215) 627-5112

CLEAR GLASSLIGHT

The unusual use by Koch & Lowy of a simple hollow glass column makes this lamp a beautiful experiment in light and reflection. The lamp is 22" high and $5^3/_8$" in diameter, and the white pleated linen shade accompanying it is 22" in diameter. White opaque glass is also available, along with 18" brass or chrome shades. The lamp takes a 150-watt incandescent bulb.

For further information, contact:

Koch & Lowy Inc.
21-24 39th Ave.
Long Island City, NY 11101
(718) 786-3520

ARNIA

Swirls of pink, straw, or white glass glow softly when the bulb housed inside the body of the Arnia table lamp is lit. Made by PAF, an Italian glass firm, and offered by Nessen, the Arnia has a ridged body complemented by a broad tissue shantung shade in black or white. The interior bulb is supplied, but the main bulb, with a maximum power of 150 watts, is not included.

Arnia comes in two sizes: 23" high and 20" wide, or $27^1/_2$" high and 23" wide.

For further information, contact:

Nessen Lamps Inc.
621 E. 216th St.
Bronx, NY 10467
(212) 231-0221

PARODIA

Piero Castiglioni has brought the headlight into the house with his Parodia lamp. A halogen bulb is housed in a 7" parabolic reflector, which in turn is mounted on a glass cylinder base. The 14"-high base comes in red, yellow, or light blue.

For more information, contact:

Interna Designs, Ltd.
The Merchandise Mart
Chicago, IL 60654
(312) 467-6076

Josef Kasparowitz

VASE LAMPS

Martin Doyle

Unlit, these table lamps by Mark McDonnell are beautiful; lit, they are even more so. The blown glass forms a sensuous vase standing either 19″ or 22″ high, as shown here. The base is made of wood and is painted black with acrylic enamel paint. McDonnell makes a wide range of vase-like table lamps and wall sconces; his work is on exhibit at several museums.

For further information about his work, contact:

Mark McDonnell
12 Rhode Island Ave.
Providence, RI 02906
(401) 331-2958

BEACON

Hap Sakwa's Beacon provides fluorescent lighting in an attractive Art Deco table lamp. The wooden base is painted with white, orange, red, and black acrylic lacquer, and the shade features layers of ⅛″-thick acrylic. The fixture measures 22″ tall overall and 8½″ wide. Beacon houses a 9-watt Sylvania fluorescent bulb.

For further information, contact:

Hap Sakwa
1330 8th St.
Baywood Park, CA 93402
(805) 528-7585

ART GLASS

Simplicity marks the shapes of Paul Hanson's blown Venetian art glass table lamps. They are available with a line of gray or red, a subtle accent of color. The sphere shown here stands 9″ high, while the flask and cylinder stand 12″ high.

For more information, contact:

Paul Hanson
610 Commercial Ave.
Carlstadt, NJ 07072
(201) 933-4873

WRIGHT LAMP

Robert Heinz, founder of Heinz & Co., has dedicated much of his efforts in recent years to reproducing the furnishings of Frank Lloyd Wright and to offering them to the general public. One example is the Prairie table lamp, designed by Wright and sharing the lines of his horizontally flaring Chicago houses. The lamp seems to be of simple construction, but it actually consists of sixty-four separate pieces.

For more information about this and other furnishings Heinz & Co. offers, contact:

Heinz & Co.
P.O. Box 663
Oak Park, IL 60303
(312) 383-1310 or (312) 960-1647

PERIELIO

With three articulated joints, this sleek reading lamp by Plana can assume

almost any position. Available in white or black, it stands 22″ high and has a base measuring 9½″. Perielio uses a halogen bulb and is equipped with a high-low switch.

For more information, contact:

Interna Designs, Ltd.
The Merchandise Mart
Chicago, IL 60654
(312) 467-6076

BUCANEVE

Bucaneve combines the delicacy of a flower-like glass shade with the solidness of a polished brass column and base. The handcrafted shades are available in pink or white, and the lamps in two sizes: 12½″ by 20″ and 19″ by 23″. Bucaneve comes with a high-low switch on the base and accommodates a 150-watt bulb. It is also available in wall sconce and chandelier models.

For further information, contact:

Nessen Lamps Inc.
621 E. 216th St.
Bronx, NY 10467
(212) 231-0221

CHIODINO

The distinctive cone-shaped Chiodino, designed by Franco Raggi, comes in several designs. Shown here is the table lamp, standing 20″ high. The bulb is halogen, and the shade is blown opal glass held by brass clamps. The base comes in either dark green or pale gray. Chiodino is also available as a floor lamp and a ceiling lamp, and all three can be adapted for outdoor use.

For further information, contact:

Interna Designs, Ltd.
The Merchandise Mart
Chicago, IL 60654
(312) 467-6076

6770 DESK LAMP

This sturdy Art Deco-style desk lamp

is designed by Robert Sonneman. Wings of polished glass stretch 17½″ across, and small columns of steel raise the fixture to 15¼″ in height. The lamp comes in either black enamel with brass details, or with red, yellow, or aqua fittings. A halogen 100-watt bulb with a full-range dimmer also comes with the lamp.

Catalogue, $2.

George Kovacs Lighting, Inc.
330 E. 59th St.
New York, NY 10022
(212) 838-3400

6411 TABLE LAMP

The 6411 table lamp by Stephen Diskin will grace a room with both handsome design and strong lighting. Its structure of balanced steel rods

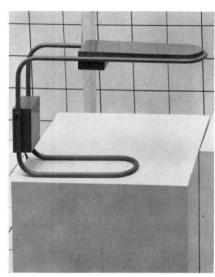

and a curved flat shade is at once elegant and simple. It uses a Norelco 13-watt fluorescent colored bulb and comes in black, white, lilac, or gray. The lamp stands 11″ tall and extends 15″. (Also available from George Kovacs is the same design in a floor lamp and a wall lamp.)

Catalogue, $2.

George Kovacs Lighting, Inc.
330 E. 59th St.
New York, NY 10022
(212) 838-3400

WINGS

Few table lamps can be compared to this one: a 10″-high column in a variety of colors with an attached wing-like shade. The shade, made of frosted, cased white glass, measures 12″ by 5″. This lamp, like other Wings models, uses a PL13-watt fluorescent bulb, the equivalent of a 60-watt incandescent bulb, except that it produces no heat and consumes 80% less energy.

For more information, contact:

Koch & Lowy Inc.
21-24 39th Ave.
Long Island City, NY 11101
(718) 786-3520

KAMSAH

Deceptively simple, Kamsah, a desk lamp from New Society and offered in the United States by Illuminating Experiences, appears to be two joined black triangles and nothing more. Inside the base, however, is a transformer which lowers the voltage and increases the current transmitted through the white supports to a 50-watt halogen bulb encased in the higher block. The lamp stands 14½" high and is 21½" long.

Catalogue, $5.

Illuminating Experiences, Inc.
107 Trumbull St.
Elizabeth, NJ 07206
(201) 527-8847

SCINTILLA TAVOLO

Fontana Arte has designed this table lamp for Interna Designs. Standing 11¾" high and 6½" wide, it is constructed of die-cast anodized aluminum in gray or black, with a stem in laquered red, yellow, or light blue. The upper section houses a halogen bulb, and the lower a transformer.

For further information, contact:

Interna Designs, Ltd.
The Merchandise Mart
Chicago, IL 60654
(312) 467-6076

DOVE

The dynamic curve of Dove's legs and the soaring line of its arm and reflector make this wireless table lamp from the Nessen/PAF collection a beautiful artifact. Designed by Mario Barbigia and Marco Columbus, Dove, available in black, houses a 50-watt halogen bulb with a high-low switch in the base. The arm pivots fully, and the legs swing around the circular base.

For further information, contact:

Nessen Lamps Inc.
621 E. 216th St.
Bronx, NY 10467
(212) 231-0221

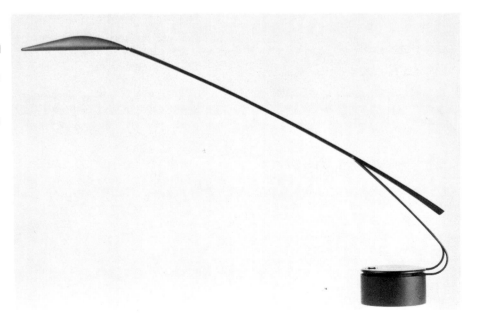

Wall Fixtures

Wall lamps have always been essential means of lighting; they save space on floors and desks, and they provide excellent ambient and direct illumination. Lamp-makers have been investigating the possibilities of design in the fixtures themselves: using stained glass in the shade, creating exotic diffusers, or turning the entire lamp into an unusual shape. Wall lamps lend themselves particularly well to these innovative designs because, situated as they are, they draw close attention to themselves much as a hanging painting does. Some craftsmen such as Mark McDonnell have explored the aesthetic possibilities of wall lamps to the point that they serve almost more for artistic purposes than those of illumination.

DECO

Deco, from Illuminating Experiences, suits its name with a rigid base, a sleek prow of cased glass, and generous amounts of polished brass for the arm and face plate. Deco supplies both bright upward lighting and softer downward lighting. The shade is available in green, cognac, white, or a satin finish. Several other models with this design are available, including a table lamp and a smaller wall bracket.

Catalogue, $5.

Illuminating Experiences, Inc.
107 Trumbull St.
Elizabeth, NJ 07206
(201) 527-8847

VENTILLA I

Innovative Products for Interiors, Inc., offers Ventilla I, a handsome wall sconce that provides upward and diffused light. The diffuser is made of ribbed, blown Murano white glass. The cradle, arm, and face plate all come in baked enamel in two colors; the face plate allows for simple attachment to a junction box.

For further information, contact:

Innovative Products for Interiors, Inc.
315 E. 62nd St.
New York, NY 10021
(212) 838-2900

LIGHT SCONCE

Ray King's early work in stained glass shapes much of his current designs in contemporary lighting. His Light Sconce has a black shade of anodized aluminum with colored lenses and color-anodized aluminum screens that filter light in irregular, cross-like patterns resembling stained glass. The sconce shown here measures 18″ high, 12″ wide, and 14″ deep.

For further information, contact:

Ray King
603 S. 10th St.
Philadelphia, PA 19147
(215) 627-5112

WALL SCONCE

Mark McDonnell mounts sensuous blown glass fixtures on either table bases or wall-sconce bases. The sconce shown here features deep shades of orange and brown with McDonnell's characteristic use of black speckles. The modified diamond back, made of black Vitrolite glass complements the spearhead-like shape of the shade. The entire fixture measures 44″ high and 18″ wide.

For further information, contact:

Mark McDonnell
12 Rhode Island Ave.
Providence, RI 02906
(401) 331-2958

AURORA

The broad, gleaming coils of glass on the Aurora wall sconce are not only beautiful, but provide excellent diffused light. The halogen bulb housed in the fixture also supplies strong upward lighting. Designed by Roberto Paimo and Renato Toso and offered by Innovative Products for Interiors, Inc., the lamp comes with a Murano glass diffuser in an assortment of colors and a baked enamel bowl, arm, and face plate in several colors as well.

For more information, contact:

Innovative Products for Interiors,
Inc.
315 E. 62nd St.
New York, NY 10021
(212) 838-2900

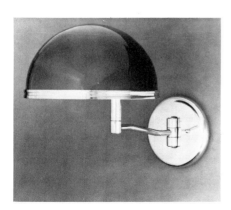

RING

The vigorous elements of glass and polished brass seem to be competing in Ring, a dynamic wall fixture from Illuminating Experiences. The shade is a smooth hemispherical dome of colored glass available in green, cognac, white, or a satin finish. Contrasting against the expansive glass is the circular band of brass with a recessed strip that emphasizes its solid construction. The swinging arm and face plate are also brass. Ring is also available in ceiling and table lamp models.

Catalogue, $5.

Illuminating Experiences, Inc.
107 Trumbull St.
Elizabeth, NJ 07206
(201) 527-8847

CORINTHIAN

Economically sculpted from white semi-glass plaster, Corinthian wall brackets draw on classical architecture and yet will do well in a contemporary setting. They can be fitted with incandescent or fluorescent bulbs and come in two sizes with heights of 7¾" and 11½".

For more information, contact:

**Boyd Lighting Company
56 Twelfth St.
San Francisco, CA 94103
(415) 431-4300**

WALL SHIELD

Ribs of crystal spread sparkling light from this Classic Illumination wall shield. Two sizes, 12" by 6" and 15" by 8", are available for the model, the metal details of which are made of either lacquered brass or chrome.

Catalogue, $3.

**The Classic Illumination, Inc.
2743 Ninth St.
Berkeley, CA 94710
(415) 849-1842**

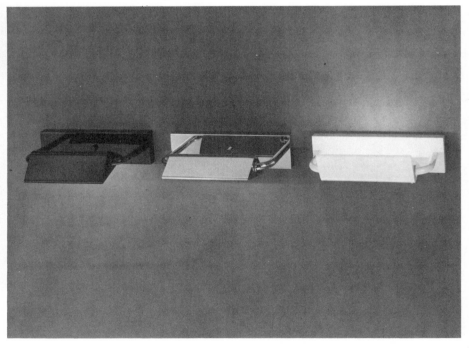

MILLELUCI

The half-tent shape and double-stem assembly of these wall brackets are not only appealingly contemporary but also useful for difficult lighting dilemmas. The Milleluci lamp, for example, can light such hard-to-reach ceilings as those in stairwells. The wall bracket is available in black, white, or polished brass, and comes with a 300-watt halogen bulb. It measures 11½" wide, and 3¼" high, and extends 8½".

Catalogue, $5.

**Illuminating Experiences, Inc.
107 Trumbull Street
Elizabeth, NJ 07206
(201) 527-8847**

BY THE SEA

These shell lights are not limited to nautical decorating schemes; the satin-white opal glass and the radiating patterns of lines go well with any post modern designs. The lamps by Koch & Lowy come in three different sizes—7" by 3½", 8½" by 4", and 10¼" by 5"—and use 75-watt bulbs.

For further information, contact:

Koch & Lowy Inc.
21-24 39th Ave.
Long Island City, NY 11101
(718) 786-3520

EGISTO WALL AND CORNER FIXTURES

Tapered wall sconces are especially popular now, but the vogue should last more than a few years. As designed by Angelo Mangiarotti, these fixtures are timeless in their elegance. Manufactured in Italy, they make use of sanded glass diffusors. Two sizes are available in the standard wall fixtures, the larger of which makes use of two 100-watt bulbs rather than one. The handy 90-degree curved corner fixture is made in only one size and will take a bulb up to 100 watts.

For further information, contact:

Artemide Inc.
150 E. 58th St.
New York, NY 10155
(212) 980-0710

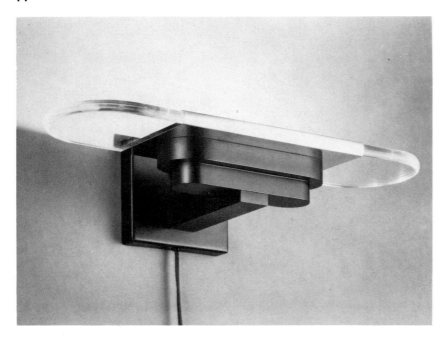

SPUN-SHAPED WALL SCONCE

The combination of gleaming metal and frosted Lucite produces an unquestionably Art Deco effect in Karl Springer's Spun-Shaped wall sconce shown here. The soft curving design of the shade also contrasts with the sharply angled base. The range of lighting fixtures offered by Karl Springer is available through designers and architects.

For more information, contact:

Karl Springer, Ltd.
305 E. 61st St.
New York, NY 10021
(212) 752-1695

6641 WALL TORCHIERE

This design by Robert Sonneman, also available in a table lamp and a floor lamp, is a sleek example of Art Deco lighting. A 16″-long slab of polished glass rests on a black module housing a 200-watt halogen bulb. The lamp has chrome or brass trim and a full-range dimmer. Its backplate is 4½″ square, and the entire fixture projects 7½″ from the wall.

Catalogue available, $2.

George Kovacs Lighting, Inc.
330 E. 59th St.
New York, NY 10022
(212) 838-3400

WALL SCONCE

The choice of a stately back for its orange and red glass shade gives Mark McDonnell's wall sconce a positively regal appearance. The shade is made of hand-blown glass and features McDonnell's distinctive tinting. Marble highlights the blue and black Vitrolite glass back, which measures 43″ by 15″.

For further information, contact:

Mark McDonnell
12 Rhode Island Ave.
Providence, RI 02906
(401) 331-2958

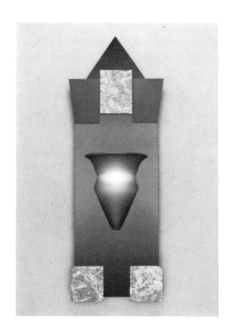

LIGHTFORMS

Fluorescent lights are almost invariably long cylinders that seem more at home in a laboratory than in one's living room. Here, though, are less intimidating wall lights, called Lightforms, with soft, spherical acrylic diffusers, preserving the advantage of fluorescent lights—their low expense —while discarding their disadvantage of unappealing looks. The Lightforms shown here are, from left to right, 10″ in diameter and 13″ high, extending 5″; 11½″ in diameter and 15¾″ high, extending 6″; and 15¼″ in diameter and 18¾″ high, extending 8″.

Catalogue, $5.

Illuminating Experiences, Inc.
107 Trumbull St.
Elizabeth, NJ 07206
(201) 527-8847

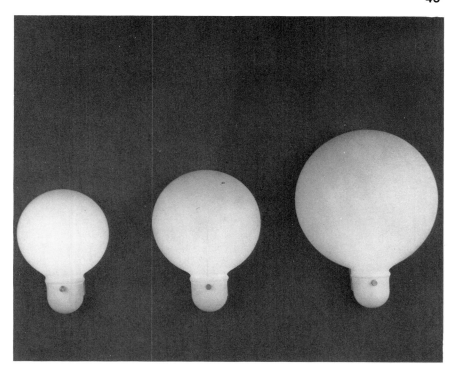

BATHROOM LIGHTS

The bright upper and side bathroom lights from Progress Lighting can illuminate all the glory (or lack thereof) of a morning face. Mounted on triangular brass bases, the lights come in groups of three or five and lengths of 19½″ or 31″.

For more information, contact:

Progress Lighting
Erie Ave. & "G" St.
Philadelphia, PA 19134
(215) 289-1200

WINGS

The distinctive curve of the Wings shade from Koch & Lowy is shown here on a wall light, but it can also be found on hanging lamps and table lamps. The shade is 12″ high and 5″ wide and is made of frosted, cased white glass. The backplate is available in a wide range of colors, and the lamp uses a PL13-watt fluorescent bulb, the equivalent of a 60-watt incandescent bulb, but much cooler and longer lasting.

For further information, contact:

Koch & Lowy Inc.
21-24 39th Ave.
Long Island City, NY 11101
(718) 786-3520

ALBA

Designed by Roberto Paimo and Renato Toso, the Alba wall lamp adds an extraordinary touch to any design. Because the diffuser, a curved glass ring, comes in a number of colors, it supplies unique lighting in different shades and intensities. The diffuser is made of hand-molded Murano glass; the arm and face plate are covered in baked enamel. Accommodating a halogen bulb, the Alba can be attached easily to a standard junction box.

For further information, contact:

Innovative Products for Interiors,
*   Inc.*
315 E. 62nd St.
New York, NY 10021
(212) 838-2900

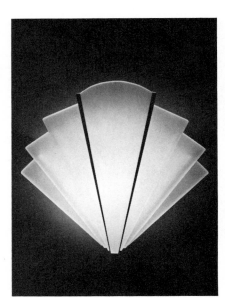

David Fishbein

LUMIA SCONCE LS 106

Plexability uses acrylic to create beautiful Art Deco wall lamps such as the Lumia Sconce. The fan-shaped fixture has mirrored details and measures 18″ in width, 16″ in length, and 8″ in depth. It is also available in custom-made sizes.

For further information, contact:

Plexability
New York Design Center, Suite #506
200 Lexington Ave.
New York, NY 10016
(212) 679-7826

ALOM/C

The 300-watt halogen bulbs housed in the attractive bowls of these lamps serve as excellent ambient lighting. The wall lamp is available in white, red, black, and brass, and comes with a cover for the bulb. The shade measures 8″ in diameter and extends 14″ from the wall. Alom/C is also available as a floor lamp.

For further information, contact:

Nessen Lamps Inc.
621 E. 216th St.
Bronx, NY 10467
(212) 231-0221

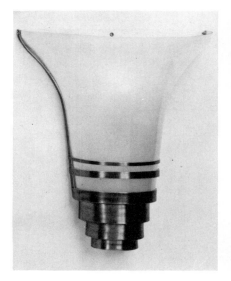

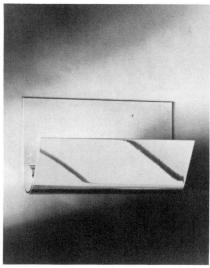

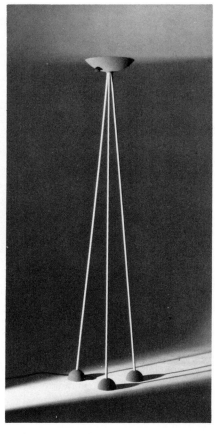

ART DECO

One of the warmer examples of postmodern Art Deco lighting is the N1386 model from Metropolitan Lighting. A 100-watt bulb burns behind a soft white plexiglass shade. Strips of polished aluminum or brass, forming the base and also highlighting the shade, add a pleasing contrast. This fixture is 17″ high overall and 14″ wide, and projects 8″ from the wall.

Catalogue available.

Metropolitan Lighting Fixture Co.
 Inc.
1010 3rd Ave.
New York, NY 10021
(212) 838-2425

WAVE

The curved plane of Wave acts as a bold highlight on any wall. Designed by Charles Gevers, the Wave lamp can accommodate fluorescent, halogen, or incandescent bulbs and comes in white enamel or a black or gray suede-like rubber-based finish. It is 7½″ high and 12″ wide, and extends 3″ from a wall.

For further information, contact:

Koch & Lowy Inc.
21-24 39th Ave.
Long Island City, NY 11101
(718) 786-3520

FOOTSTEPS

The spidery torchiere, Footsteps, is one of the few floor lamps that does not consist of a single column. Three cup-like feet with gray suede-like finishes support a bowl-shaped shade at a height of 74″. The shade is available in black or gray or in chrome or brass. The legs come in black or yellow enamel. Footsteps is equipped with a full-range dimmer and can accommodate a 500-watt halogen bulb.

For more information, contact:

Koch & Lowy Inc.
21-24 39th Ave.
Long Island City, NY 11101
(718) 786-3520

Floor Lamps

Torchieres are becoming more and more tall and slender. While generally supplying excellent light with halogen bulbs, these lamps are very much artistic experiments in elongated lines. The shades on some floor lamps have even been shrinking in order to em- *phasize the long tubing. While this tendency may present a difficulty for a consumer looking for a subdued floor lamp, the possibilities for many contemporary homes remains quite exciting.*

TORCHIERE

The Touchtronic system, which allows you to turn on a light by merely touching the lamp, making a switch unneccessary, seems to be one of the last steps along the way to transform-

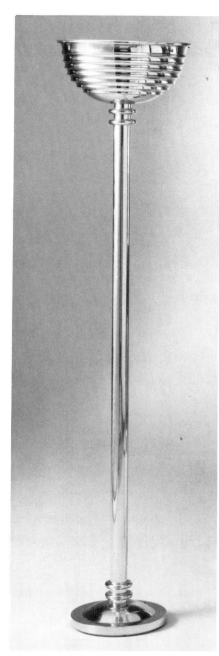

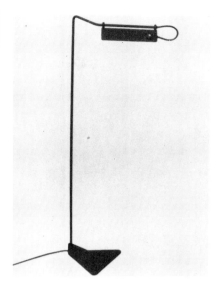

DELTA FLUORESCENT

While attractive, the Delta Fluorescent floor lamp is seriously practical. Designed by Piotr Sierakowski for Koch & Lowy, the light has a non-reflective, scratch-resistant finish in black or gray. It stands 44″ high and has an 8¼″ by 2½″ shade which can pivot 360° around the lamp arm. Within the shade is a chrome reflector and a PL9-watt bulb, producing light equivalent to that of a regular 60-watt bulb, but using 80% less energy, giving off no heat, and burning for 10,000 hours.

For more information, contact:

Koch & Lowy Inc.
21-24 39th Ave.
Long Island City, NY 11101
(718) 786-3520

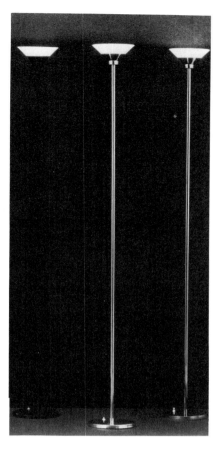

SPATS

This extremely slender torchiere stands 69″ in height and has a base of 8″ in diameter. The shade is of opal glass, 7½″ in diameter, and takes a 150-watt halogen bulb. The lamp comes in polished brass, chrome, white, or black, and has a foot switch on its base.

For further information, contact:

Koch & Lowy Inc.
21-24 39th Ave.
Long Island City, NY 11101
(718) 786-3520

ing torchieres such as this one into pure sculpture and craftsmanship, without any worry over overt mechanical needs. This lamp (model #1984), made of polished brass by Paul Hanson, stands 70″ high and has a ribbed shade.

For further information, contact:

Paul Hanson
610 Commercial Ave.
Carlstadt, NJ 07072
(201) 933-4873

BEAM

The Beam floor lamp, designed by Enrico Bona, incorporates strong geometric elements into its appearance, especially the origami-like stem and reflector. The halogen bulb supplies upward and diffused light and is controlled by a dimmer along the side of the lamp. Made of extruded aluminum, the lamp is available in four different colors, while its metal base comes only in black. As shown here, the Beam is also available as a ceiling or a wall fixture.

For further information, contact:

Innovative Products for Interiors, Inc.
315 E. 62nd St.
New York, NY 10021
(212) 838-2900

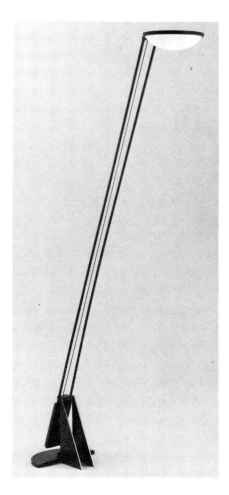

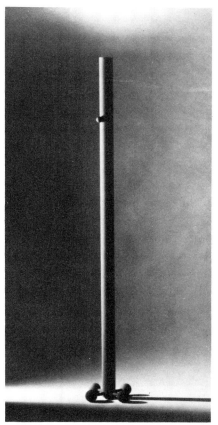

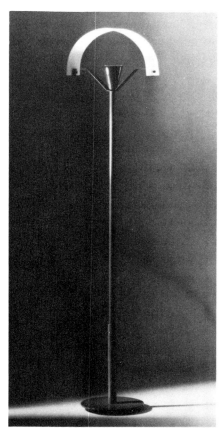

TRUCK

"Swan" might be a more appropriate name for the almost eerie elongated elegance of this floor lamp by New Society. Standing 75½" high when upright and as low as 68" when fully tilted at 45° (moving 33" away from the base), this lamp is designed so that the bulb always remains in a horizontal position. It uses a 250-watt halogen bulb in an etched glass diffuser; an in-line floor dimmer controls its intensity. Truck is available in black or white.

Catalogue, $5.

Illuminating Experiences, Inc.
107 Trumbull St.
Elizabeth, NJ 07206
(201) 527-8847

EAGLE

Piotr Sierakowski has designed a light column whose similarity to a gun barrel is heightened by its availability in either a gray or black rubber-based material. The column is 72" high, and the base, composed of four knobs, is 9" wide. A dimmer knob on the side of the column controls the halogen bulb within this most simple of functional designs.

For further information, contact:

Koch & Lowy Inc.
21-24 39th Ave.
Long Island City, NY 11101
(718) 786-3520

CILOSTER

Koch & Lowy manufactures the Ciloster 250-watt halogen torchiere which is equipped with an arch of frosted glass to diffuse the light. It is available with a black or red and gray finish and stands 76" high. The 12" base has an on-off foot switch.

For further information, contact:

Koch & Lowy Inc.
21-24 39th Ave.
Long Island City, NY 11101
(718) 786-3520

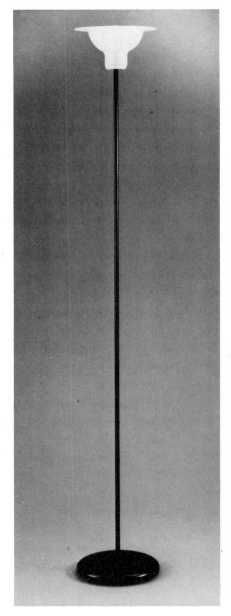

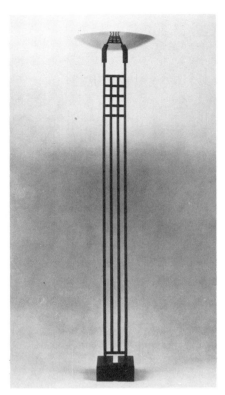

diffuser is also available as a pendant lamp.

Catalogue, $5.

Illuminating Experiences, Inc.
107 Trumbull St.
Elizabeth, NJ 07206
(201) 527-8847

BELLISSIMA

Bellissima by Koch & Lowy serves well both as a chairside reading lamp and as a room light. It can be raised from 35″ to 47″ in height and has an adjustable 6″ shade at the end of a 14¾″ arm. The base is 6″ by 9″. The lamp comes in polished brass, chrome, or California brass, and uses a 100-watt bulb and a full-range dimmer.

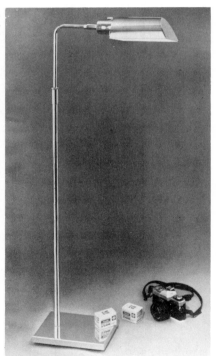

For further information, contact:

Koch & Lowy Inc.
21-24 39th St.
Long Island City, NY 11101
(718) 786-3520

VEART

The Italian glass blowers of VeArt have developed a unique torchiere. Standing 72″ high, the lamp is capped by a satin glass diffuser. Parallel flat metal rods support the lamp and also frame the electric cord. While the bulb is not supplied with the lamp, Illuminating Experiences offers separately a 250-watt Edison base halogen bulb that suits the lamp well. Conventional light bulbs are also usable. The standing lamp comes in both black and white, and the broad

6520 TORCHIERE

Standing 69″ high, this torchiere, designed by Robert Sonneman for George Kovacs Lighting, has the strength of composition and structure one would associate with classical architecture. Four black columns rise from a black base and join near the top in a grid. A 16″-wide disk-like shade of polished brass adds the finishing touch. The lamp uses a 400-watt halogen bulb and has a full-range dimmer.

Catalogue, $2.

George Kovacs Lighting, Inc.
330 E. 59th St.
New York, NY 10022
(212) 838-3400

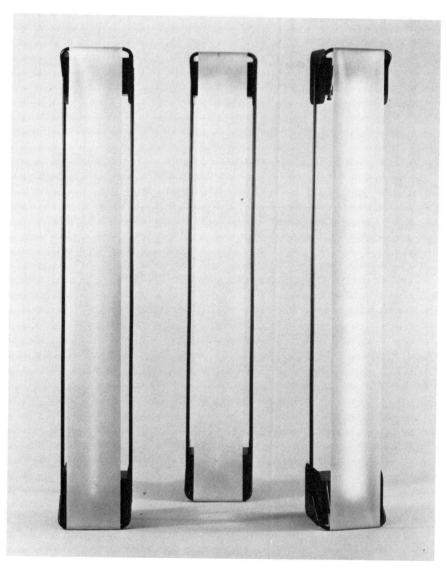

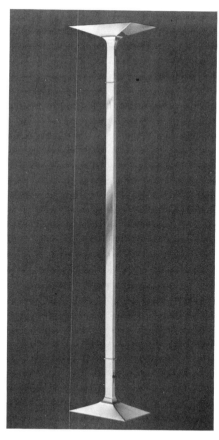

MAGIA

Made by New Society and sold by Illuminating Experiences, Inc., Magia is less a lighting instrument than sculpture, crafted from polished brass and standing 68″ high. A contemporary interpretation of torch lights popular in the 1930s, it uses a 500-watt halogen bulb, which is included, and also has a dimmer.

Catalogue, $5.

Illuminating Experiences, Inc.
107 Trumbull St.
Elizabeth, NJ 07206
(201) 527-8847

LN-15

Dan Chelsea designed this floor lamp for George Kovacs Lighting. A uniquely modern effect is created by the stretching of white diffusing material in front of a neon bulb and a 300-watt halogen "uplight." The 68″-high frame is made of black steel, and the neon is available in blue, red, or aqua.

Catalogue, $2.

George Kovacs Lighting, Inc.
330 E. 59th St.
New York, NY 10022
(212) 838-3400

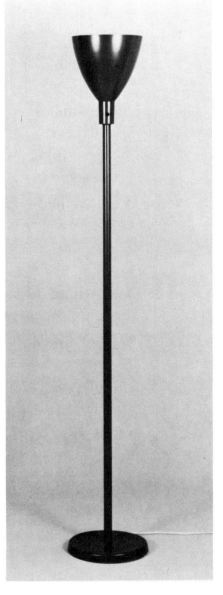

LN-1 NEON TORCH

The neon and halogen lights in this futuristic lamp, designed by Dan Chelsea, are a distinctly contemporary combination. The neon tube, which wraps around two sides of the square column, is available in blue, white, orchid, or red, and the 400-watt halogen bulb inside the fixture comes with a full-range dimmer. The black anodized aluminum column is 4″ square and 72″ high.

Catalogue, $2.

George Kovacs Lighting, Inc.
330 E. 59th St.
New York, NY 10022
(212) 838-3400

6706 TORCHIERE

In either white or gray, the torchiere designed by Peter Hamburger provides both ambient lighting and beautiful composition. The tulip-shaped shade measures 8¾″ across and the entire lamp 66″ high. The lamp can accommodate a three-way bulb as powerful as 250 watts.

Catalogue, $2.

George Kovacs Lighting, Inc.
330 E. 59th St.
New York, NY 10022
(212) 838-3400

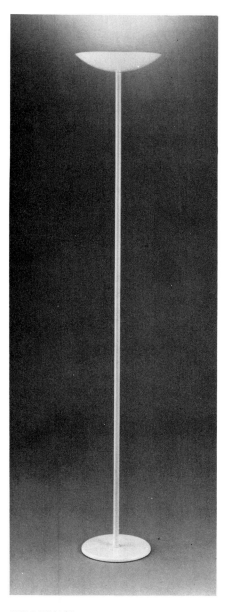

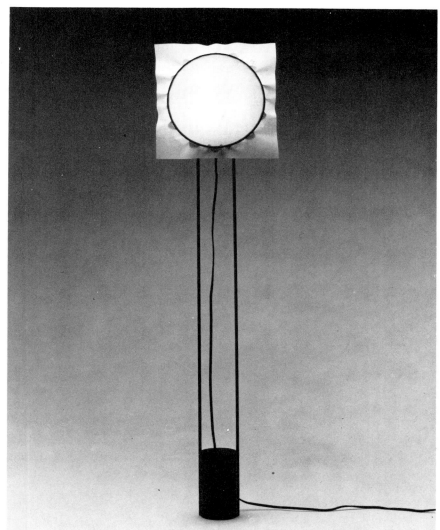

MILLELUCI

Each standing 72″ high, the Milleluci line of floor lamps is pleasingly simple. Available in white on steel, as shown here, or black on steel or polished brass, Milleluci lamps use a 300-watt halogen bulb and come with a foot-controlled switch.

Catalogue, $5.

Illuminating Experiences, Inc.
107 Trumbull St.
Elizabeth, NJ 07206
(201) 527-8847

CORONA LAMP

Lorenzo Porchelli designed this ultra-contemporary floor lamp in 1981; the Museum of Modern Art now offers it. A striking effect is created by shading the bulb with a sheet of rice paper fixed by a steel ring. The resulting corona of diffused light gives the fixture its name. The steel and aluminum frame, given a black enamel finish, stands 52½″ high.

Catalogue, $2.

Mail Order Department
Museum of Modern Art
11 W. 53rd Street
New York, NY 10019
(212) 708-9888

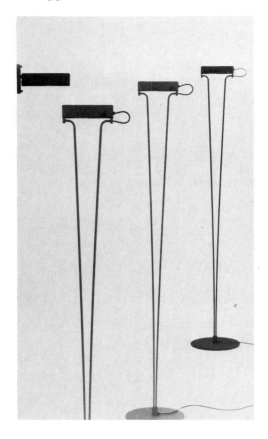

reflector bulbs, the "uplights," as they are called in the trade, cast a sharp beam to illuminate artwork or to add an imaginative streak to a room's design. The lights shown here are 5″ in diameter; 6″ models using 75-watt bulbs, are also available.

Catalogue, $2.

George Kovacs Lighting, Inc.
330 E. 59th St.
New York, NY 10022
(212) 838-3400

DELTA HALOGEN

Similar to the Delta Fluorescent model illustrated earlier in this section, this floor lamp has branching arms on which the shade rests, making it as attractive as serviceable. It stands 73″ high and comes in black or gray suede-like material which is non-reflective and scratch resistant. The 8¼″ by 2½″ shade pivots 45° and uses a 500-watt halogen bulb.

For further information, contact:

Koch & Lowy Inc.
21-24 39th Ave.
Long Island City, NY 11101
(718) 786-3520

FOOTLIGHTS

Not all floor lights have to be six-foot-tall torchieres. Resting on black tripods, these small, ball-shaped floor lamps can provide lighting in just about any direction. With 50-watt

Hanging and Ceiling Fixtures

Hanging lamps are the most popular and stylish of ceiling-attached fixtures. Dominated for some time by an oligarchy of conically and spherically shaped lamps and by the latter-day popularity of tiered glass-and-brass Art Deco creations, the current array of hanging lamps is incorporating new and neglected designs worth noting. Chandeliers, for example, are finding a new look, and fluorescent and halogen lighting now serve the demands of

hanging lamps with originality and brilliance. On the other hand, recessed ceiling lamps still remain generally unattractive and track lighting cliché if not passé, but an innovative model is included in this section for each of these lighting forms. With the refreshingly varied array of styles available, a consumer can find the right atmosphere-setting fixture for any room, from a brightly lit kitchen to a softly illuminated dining room.

VAN

Innovative Products for Interiors, Inc., offers an elegant alternative to the normal array of bland recessed lighting. The Van, a ceiling fixture designed by Roberto Paimo for I.P.I., provides downward light through the clear glass at the center and more subdued light through the ring of

frosted glass. The recessed housing is suitable for virtually any type of ceiling.

For more information, contact:

Innovative Products for Interiors, Inc.
315 E. 62nd St.
New York, NY 10021
(212) 838-2900

MICRO-SIZED TRACK LIGHTING

Shown here are three examples of Progress Lighting's new line of small, powerful track lamps. Only between 3″ and 4″ in total diameter, the fixtures have 120-volt MR-16 lamps with reflectors, creating a strong beam of well-directed white light. Such lighting is excellent for displaying artwork or imaginatively illuminating a room. Progress Lighting offers a wide range of styles and colors for these lights, all of which can be turned 360° horizontally and 90° vertically.

For more information, contact:

Progress Lighting
Erie Avenue & "G" St.
Philadelphia, PA 19134
(215) 289-1200

WINGS

Doing justice to its name, this hanging lamp exudes a feeling of motion in the bend of its stem and the curve of its shade. The frosted, cased white glass shade measures 12″ by 5″ and is also available as a table or wall lamp. The stem is available in either a white enamel or a suede-like black rubber-based finish. Wings uses a PL13-watt fluorescent bulb, the equivalent of a 75-watt incandescent bulb, but much more economical and cool.

For further information, contact:

Koch & Lowy Inc.
21-24 39th Ave.
Long Island City, NY 11101
(718) 786-3520

ART DECO N1376

Layers of plexiglass and brushed aluminum disks simulate the Art Deco style in this fixture from Metropolitan Lighting. The N1376 model is 21″ in diameter and is 29″ in overall height. One 150-watt bulb fits inside the assembly, which is accented with polished chrome or brass.

Catalogue available.

Metropolitan Lighting Fixture Co. Inc.
1010 Third Ave.
New York, NY 10021
(212) 838-2425

SCINTILLA B. T. ZOMMATORIA

Designed by Fontana Arte, this hanging lamp is unique and has as much merit in novelty as in usefulness for creating a mood through light. Small halogen bulbs are housed in units built so as to be connected loosely to other units by copper rods in a chain. Glass rods with eyes are used to insure stability, and a chrome-plated brass ball caps off the series to guarantee electrical contact. The owner of such a lamp can extend it with rods and bulbs to comprise

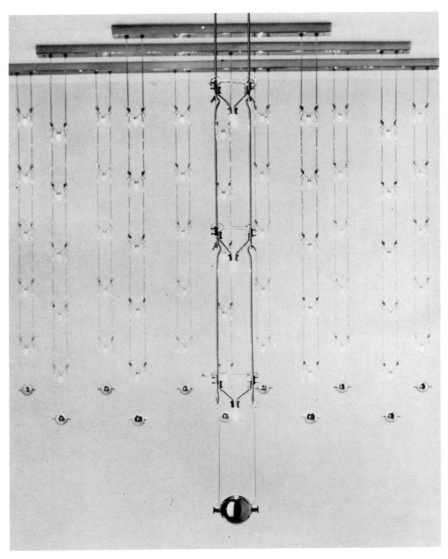

Koch & Lowy Inc.
21-24 39th Ave.
Long Island City, NY 11101
(718) 786-3520

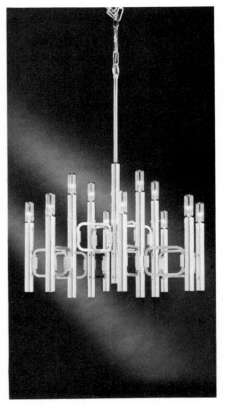

twelve lights. A transformer is available for this model.

For further information, contact:

Interna Designs, Ltd.
The Merchandise Mart
Chicago, IL 60654
(312) 467-6076

MODULO

Designed by Aldo Marchetti of Rome, this brass sculpture is a modern response to the chandelier form of earlier years. Opposing elements are beautifully set against each other in the fixture: the polished-brass and satin-brass highlights create a contrasting finish, and the vertical tubes (heightened with bulbs provided with your order) act to oppose the horizontal joining pieces. Marchetti's design also comes in models with three or six lights. The fixture shown here is 23″ in diameter and 19″ high.

Catalogue, $5.

Illuminating Experiences, Inc.
107 Trumbull St.
Elizabeth, NJ 07206
(201) 527-8847

SIBILLA

The Sibilla lamp from Koch & Lowy is simply a beautiful object. Venetian glass blowers combine several layers of glass into an obsidian-like shade with a slender orange line beveled into it. The shade is 22″ in diameter and 7½″ high and holds a cased white glass diffuser, accommodating two 100-watt bulbs.

For more information, contact:

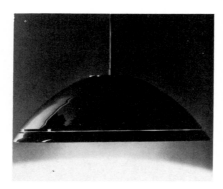

KANTHOS

A new pendant from Boyd Lighting, Kanthos boasts scalloped, upswept petals of white semigloss plaster. In each pendant is set a section of translucent opal glass which provides soft light downwards. Kanthos comes in two sizes (either 28″ or 48″ in diameter) and uses either four or six 100-watt bulbs.

For more information, contact:

***Boyd Lighting Company
56 Twelfth St.
San Francisco, CA 94103
(415) 431-4300***

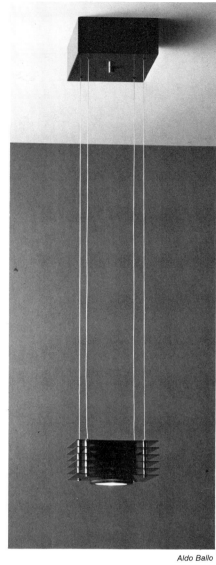

Aldo Ballo

HEIRLOOM

The simple practicality of a brass bowl pendant lamp is reinterpreted here by Fausto dalla Torre. This solid polished-brass fixture is 12½″ in diameter and 10″ high. It is also available in un-polished "vintage" brass.

Catalogue, $5.

***Illuminating Experiences, Inc.
107 Trumbull St.
Elizabeth, NJ 07206
(201) 527-8847***

HIKARY

Even the wiring adds to the design of the Hikary hanging lamp designed by Ettore Sottsass, Jr., and offered in the United States by Innovative Products for Interiors, Inc. The halogen bulb is housed in a tiered box coated in baked enamel and with a glass dif-fuser. The cables, which can extend up to 36″, lead up to a ceiling box that mounts on a standard junction box.

For further information, contact:

***Innovative Products for Interiors,
  Inc.
315 E. 62nd St.
New York, NY 10021
(212) 838-2900***

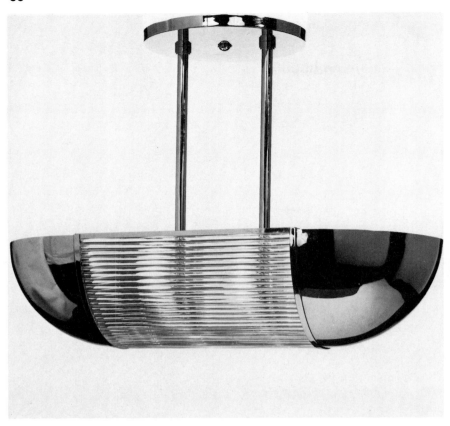

ART DECO N1362

The massiveness of this lamp from Metropolitan Lighting (32″ in length and 16″ in width) can prove the crowning touch to a large room with an Art Deco motif in its design. Six 60-watt bulbs provide bright ambient and ceiling lighting, and the ribbed glass underside allows for softer and more direct light as well. This lamp also has chrome ends and base and is supported by 24″-high glass rods.

Catalogue available.

Metropolitan Lighting Fixture Co. Inc.
1010 Third Ave.
New York, NY 10021
(212) 838-2425

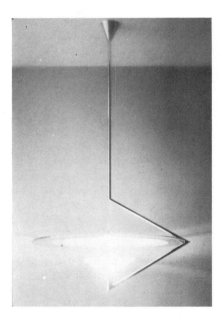

OLAMPIA

It's almost as if the Olampia had wanted to be a torchiere: the chrome-plated tube descends from the ceiling several feet before turning back on itself. Thus a hanging lamp produces torchiere light, modified by a disk of sand-blasted glass 28½″ wide. Designed by Fontana Arte, it uses a halogen bulb and a shade in white opal glass.

For further information, contact:

Interna Designs, Ltd.
The Merchandise Mart
Chicago, IL 60654
(312) 467-6076

GIO PONTI

Layers of either clear crystal or sand-blasted glazed crystal direct the light of Gio Ponti into beautiful patterns. Designed by Fontana Arte, the 21″ hanging lamp houses three 60-watt bulbs in the central cylinder of glazed crystal glass. The entire assembly is mounted and trimmed in chrome or brass.

For further information, contact:

Interna Designs, Ltd.
The Merchandise Mart
Chicago, IL 60654
(312) 467-6076

Paul Aresu

TIERED CHANDELIER

In one of its latest incarnations, the chandelier, as designed by Michael Zevy Berkowicz, is an inverted pyramid of frosted acrylic disks around a central post. The Art Deco fixture measures 33" in diameter and 8" in height, and accommodates six bulbs.

For more information about this fixture and other acrylic specialties of Plexability, contact:

Plexability
New York Design Center
200 Lexington Ave.
New York, NY 10016
(212) 679-7826

CONTEMPORARY CLASSICS

This hanging stem lamp (#14BLI), available as a matching floor lamp (#14BI) as well, displays a gracefully curving 14" shade in blown cased glass in black or white. The body is made of brass.

Catalogue, $3.

The Classic Illumination, Inc.
2743 Ninth St.
Berkeley, CA 94710
(415) 849-1842

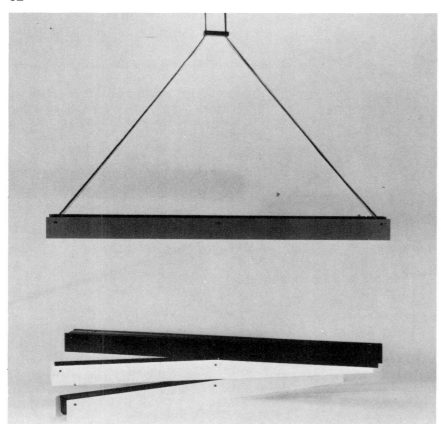

HANGING FLUORESCENT LIGHTING

Fluorescent lighting never dangled like this before. Designed by Robert Sonneman, these 25-watt lamps come with six feet of aircraft cable to hang them at almost any desired height. They are made of enameled steel, come in black, white, red, or yellow, and measure 40″ by 3¼″ by 2⅝″.

Catalogue, $2.

George Kovacs Lighting, Inc.
330 E. 59th St.
New York, NY 10022
(212) 838-3400

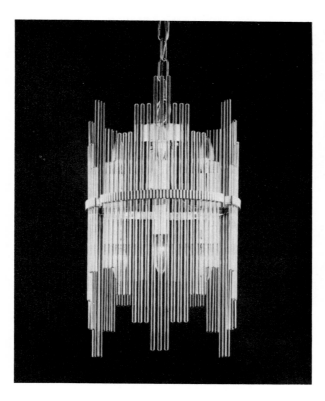

DIADEM

Lights pointed both up and down behind a shield of crystal rods produce a shimmering effect that can alone set a mood. Designed by Sciolari of Rome, this chandelier and other fixtures in the Diadem series are well suited for lighting entrances, dining rooms, and hallways. The model illustrated here is 11″ in diameter and 20″ high, and uses six bulbs with up to 60 watts of power.

Catalogue, $5.

Illuminating Experiences, Inc.
107 Trumbull St.
Elizabeth, NJ 07206
(201) 527-8847

Other Suppliers of Lighting

Consult List of Suppliers for addresses.

Floor Lamps

Alpha Design Studio, Inc.
Artemide Inc.
Atelier International Ltd.
Boyd Lighting Co.
Brayton International Collection
Calger
The Classic Illumination, Inc.
Interna Designs, Ltd.
Lighting Associates Inc.
Cy Mann Designs
Nessen Lamps Inc.
Plexability
Ron Rezek/Lighting
Roche Bobois
Scandinavian Design Inc.
Thunder & Light

Hanging and Ceiling Fixtures

Ambience
Artemide Inc.
Atelier International Ltd.
Audio Design Associates
Brayton International Collection
Calger
Elliptipar
Greene's Lighting Fixtures
Habitat Inc.
Paul Hanson
Lazin Lighting

Lighting Associates Inc.
Lightolier, Inc.
Lightworks
Lithonia Downlighting
Cy Mann Designs
Nessen Lamps Inc.
Plexability
Rambusch
Joseph Richter, Inc.
Thunder & Light
Trakliting Inc.
Wasley Lighting Inc.

Table Lamps

Architectural Pottery
Artemide Inc.
Atelier International Ltd.
Boyd Lighting Co.
Brayton International Collection
Calger
The Classic Illumination, Inc.
Hilo Steiner
House of Troy
Lighting Associates Inc.
Cy Mann Designs
Plexability
Ron Rezek/Lighting
Thunder & Light

Wall Fixtures

Ambience
Atelier International Ltd.
Calger
Habitat Inc.
Paul Hanson
Interna Designs, Ltd.
Let There Be Neon
Lighting Associates Inc.
Lightolier Inc.
Lithonia Downlighting
Cy Mann Designs
Rambusch
Ron Rezek/Lighting
Joseph Richter, Inc.
Thunder & Light
Wasley Lighting Inc.

3.

Kitchens and Baths

Functionalism, efficiency, and utility are catchwords which come quickly to mind when describing an ideal kitchen or bath—the two rooms in any house or apartment which most require modernity. And it is in such areas that twentieth-century contemporary design has left its greatest mark. Since the 1930s the design of kitchens and baths has kept pace with advances in technology, improvements which have contributed immeasurably to the ease of daily life. As one appliance or fixture has been added to another, the lines of the modern kitchen and bath have emerged. From the first freestanding appliances have come streamlined modular designs which incorporate several functions; from a potpourri of gadgets have come what designers now call systems for storing and using these objects.

Is there now anything left to explore? The pace of technological change has slowed somewhat, but the flow of electronic gadgetry continues. And there is an even greater need for convenient storage space in both the kitchen and the bath. Change in the arrangement of these rooms, however, is now more a result of how they are used rather than of what is used in them. The kitchen is increasingly an area for eating and entertaining as well as cooking; the bath is now recommended as a place to relax and not only to shower and shave.

The new kitchen and bath designs, especially from European suppliers, emphasize these new uses. Considerable attention is given to the selection of colors and finishes used in cabinets, appliances, and fixtures. Provision is made for effective, quiet ventilation in the kitchen so that it is a pleasant place in which to dine or to entertain. Bath designs include such features as saunas, hot tubs, and special showering devices.

Since these rooms are increasingly being used for multiple purposes, their design is being streamlined even further. Not since the 1930s have modular designs been as much in vogue. American manufacturers pioneered in the design of modern kitchens and baths, but, in the 1980s, the impetus for change is coming from Europe, especially West Germany. The signs of change, however, are already visible on the North American front.

AEG cook top and oven installation.

Kitchen Designs and Appliances

Attractiveness derives almost completely from function in a kitchen. Holding a boiling pot of water, one has a very short supply of artistic appreciation, and, under the circumstances, a cabinet with charming detailing is worthless compared to one you can bang shut with an elbow. Efficiency and compactness can still be aesthetic ideals. Several of the kitchens illustrated in this section, for example, have been almost symphonically designed and are beautiful in their sensible imaginativeness. Ideally, appliances such as ovens and sinks also keep out of one's way, and out of their unobtrusiveness comes a sleek elegance. In the kitchen, more than anywhere else in the house, foresight is essential. Here, as in the bath, European designers are leading the way.

ABBAKA

Abbaka imports Juvel sinks from Denmark. These sinks, designed for kitchens and bars, are made of brass, stainless steel, or enamel-coated mild steel. They are available in other conventionally rectangular models or in seamless round shapes.

Owners of stainless-steel sinks such as the circular one shown here (the C313E model) can choose between either a satin or mirror finish. Stainless steel with a mirror finish is especially attractive, resembling conventional chrome plating. Chrome, however, reveals the brass underneath when scratched, while stainless steel remains virtually unmarked. The model shown measures 12½" in diameter and 6" in depth. Other models have a wider diameter or drain, and all are made from 18-gauge, 18/10 non-magnetic chromium nickel steel. The teak chopping board shown here, as well as chrome strainers, comes as an accessory to these models.

The Juvel 0340D shown here, a com-bined sink and drainboard, is made of brass polished to a mirror finish and measures 28½" long and 16½" wide. The sink, 13½" long, 11⅞" wide, and 5" deep, has a garbage disposal.

The combination of the 0 40/40 white enamel sink and Bormix 80 black enamel faucet demonstrates the potential attractiveness of a fixture as pragmatic as the kitchen sink. Made of 18-gauge steel, this and other similar models come in a range of enamel colors (brass, black, white, red, or brown). Several accessories are supplied with the sink, including fitted teak or beech chopping boards, a plastic-coated drainer basket, and a colander.

For further information, contact:

Abbaka
435 23rd St.
San Francisco, CA 94107
(415) 648-7210

Lawrence Williams

Ernest Silva, Inc.

AMERICAN OLEAN TILES

American Olean brings tiles to the forefront in kitchen design. Olean tile can work with virtually any surface—the kitchen island shown here is capped by black ceramic tile. Not only is the black surface a beautiful contrast to the white floor tiles, but it can withstand the abuse that any kitchen surface must endure.

The pinstripe-style tiling also illustrated here actually defines the space in the kitchen. Set in differing directions on the floor and walls, 2″ by 1″ ebony and 2″ by 2″ white porcelain tiles give the rather long room a more expansive feeling. The room's design becomes energetic as the thin striping elegantly offsets the block-shaped fixtures in the kitchen.

For further information, contact:

***American Olean Tiles
1000 Cannon Ave.
Landsdale, PA 19446-0271
(215) 855-1111***

KOHLER

Kohler offers a number of small and moderately-sized sinks for those who need to be miserly with space.

The Urbanite packs in most of the features one would expect on a large double-bowl sink. Measuring only 25″ by 22″, the self-rimming, single-bowl sink can be easily installed in today's typical apartment kitchen which some might mistake for a closet. The integrated garbage basin is elevated to an easy reach and the enamel cast-iron sink, shown here, is equipped with a Triton II faucet and spray.

Kohler's Gibson sink makes economical use of space, either in the kitchen or as part of a bar to facilitate the preparation of drinks. The acrylic sink measures 25″ by 15″ and features a cutting board and steel cups for garnishes, all set in the fixture.

For further information, contact:

Kohler Co.
Kohler, WI 53044
(414) 457-4441

RUTT CUSTOM KITCHENS

While other firms emphasize sleekness or dazzling compartmentalization in their custom-made kitchens, Rutt takes particular pride in solidness and durability. Rutt makes both contemporary and traditional cabinetry, and the careful attention to workmanship is evident in both. Rutt also warns design dilettantes away from their products; they believe that their customers should be as serious about excellence as they are.

The long process of making Rutt cabinets begins with the kiln-drying of lumber so that it will not expand or contract excessively when finally installed. Rutt hand-fits doors and drawers as a precaution against binding and sticking. The doors are well-balanced so as to need only a touch to close, and ball-bearing nylon rollers on four-track metal slides in the drawers result in silent opening and closing.

Rutt cabinet shelves can resist nearly any of the typical kitchen hazards. They are treated against scratches, moisture, heat, and stains. In addition, Rutt tests them to support six times the weight that normal kitchen shelves can. The shelves can be adjusted in ½″ increments of height.

To complement their cabinets, Rutt makes a wide range of accessories. Among these custom-built products are shelves that rotate 180° for twice the usual storage space, folding-out ironing boards, wire racks, and chopping blocks.

Shown here is one of Rutt's more contemporary designs, the Copenhagen. Rutt calls it a "transition" design, and one can see how these cabinets and other fixtures blend a solid, old-fashioned quality with the clean, uncluttered look of contemporary design. Shown here in ivory oak, these beveled front panels are also available in cherry.

For more information, contact:

Rutt Custom Kitchens
Rte. 23
Goodville, PA 17528
(215) 445-6751

contemporary cabinets. For Design Group 84, Wood-Mode adopted the new European style of frameless construction, maintaining the quality of their traditional cabinets. The doors are hinged on the inside so that they swing open 125°, and the interior of all of the Design 84 cabinets are finished with a melamine laminate in a light, neutral color. Wood-Mode also makes a large variety of accessories for their cabinets, such as specialized shelving and wine racks.

Alpha and Vanguard, two of the six designs in this line, are shown here. Alpha draws its inspiration from Northern European styles, with smooth horizontal rails of oak highlighted by brass handles. These cabinets are made of solid wood in a tongue-and-groove construction. The cleanness of these lines complements a number of contemporary styles, including post-modern Art Deco.

Vanguard's white laminate cabinet doors and counter tops form a group of virtually uninterrupted planes, making for a very contemporary style. It also comes in other colors of laminates and oak veneers. Combined with various hardware options, this kitchen design leaves the homeowner a great deal of liberty to create his own look.

For more information about the Design 84 group of cabinets, contact:

Wood-Mode Cabinetry
Kreamer, PA 17833
(717) 374-2711

WOOD-MODE CABINETRY

Wood-Mode, founded in 1942, makes cabinets for every part of the house—dining rooms, studies, bedrooms, and living rooms, as well as kitchens.

Their products fall into two distinct categories: the Design Group 42 of traditional styles of woodworking; and the Design Group 84, a new line of

GAGGENAU

As our daily diet has become enriched with a greater variety of foods and new ways to prepare them, the technology of cooking has undergone significant changes. Not since the widespread adoption of electric appliances in the 1920s and '30s has so much attention been devoted to food preparation. Now in the 1980s we have gone beyond such time-saving gimmicks as the Cuisinart and the microwave oven and are reassessing the use of basic appliances. The North American kitchen is being Europeanized, and the German firm of Gaggenau is playing a major role in the redesign of this most important of domestic spaces.

Gaggenau produces a line of technically advanced appliances—stoves, ventilating hoods, sinks, and ovens—which is as aesthetically appealing as it is practical. The kitchen illustrated here makes use of these basic elements. Typically, they are

hardly visible, and are tucked away in convenient locations amid the ample counter space. The designers at Gaggenau are well aware that cooking is an activity that requires very thoughtful planning, and that the modern kitchen is often a dining area as well. Efficiency and comfort must go hand in hand.

The ventilating hood design is indicative of the careful consideration given the important function of exhausting cooking heat and odors. The main section of the hood is a small rectangular box which fits easily between two cabinets, ample storage space being left above it. The hood is equipped with a retractable steam visor that can be pushed back flush with the surrounding cabinet units when not in use. The visor is thoughtfully fitted with a transparent glass insert so that when the device is pulled out, the cooking surface is not blocked from view.

The hood is extremely quiet in operation and is powered by two electrically controlled fan motors. There are four speeds. Both this model—250—and a smaller unit without the steam visor, make use of a metal grease filter which can be washed easily. And both may be used as a self-contained unit (with charcoal filter) or vented.

Gaggenau stove units can be incorporated into cabinet space or paired with an oven. Illustrated is one of the medium-size installations with a glass ceramic cooktop unit, two electric rings, a ventilation unit, and a barbecue grill. Both the glass and burner units measure only $11^5/_{16}''$ by $20^1/_{16}''$, yet there is more than sufficient room to position several medium-size vessels. Just as important, the very slim units require only a small area of cabinet space below. The electric grill has the same surface dimensions and extends only $3^1/_8''$ below the surface.

If your local kitchen or home center has not caught up with the times and is unable to supply you with further information regarding Gaggenau appliances and accessories, contact:

**Gaggenau USA Corp.
5 Commonwealth Ave.
Woburn, Mass. 01801
(617) 938-1655**

In addition to the two-element glass ceramic and the two-burner electric units, there are also two-burner gas units, four-burner electric or gas units, four-burner combination gas and electric units, and four-burner glass ceramic cooktops.

The units shown are in stainless steel, but they come as well in white, brown, sand, and almond enamel finishes.

Among the special appliances that can be used with a cooktop—in addition to the barbecue grill—are a surface ventilating unit and an electric deep fryer. Both require more space underneath the cooking surface than the burner units, but the depth is no more than 13$^{11}/_{16}$″. The ventilator must be vented outside or into a flue.

Gaggenau's five oven models are all electric. Interestingly, this highly advanced firm has not invested in microwave technology but prefers the

slower cooking qualities of a conventional system which is supplemented with a circulating hot-air device that can be switched on and off as desired. This convection device is especially useful for thawing frozen foods. It will also speed up cooking time, but not at the expense of the food.

Recently added to the Gaggenau line are single and double sinks in the same colors—white, brown, sand, and almond—featured in the cooktop units. These are of steel fabrication and are finished in acid- and chip-resistant enamel. Shown here are two single units, a deep sink fitted with an optional crockery basket or portable drainer, and a shallow sink used for preparing foods. The standard single sink, not shown here, is fitted with a drainer that has its own drain. The standard double-sink is made up of a large and a small unit as well as a drainer that drains into the small sink.

AEG

Ovens made by AEG of Germany are unobtrusive and practically invisible among the other features of a kitchen, as they blend into the surrounding design of cabinets and appliances. In addition to being crucial in small kitchens with little space to spare, these ovens, available in six colors, can be a strong addition to a kitchen's design.

For further information, contact:

Andi-Co.
2100 N. Central Rd., Suite 301
Fort Lee, NJ 07024
(201) 585-9362

POGGENPOHL

You will find thoughtfulness in the choice of every fixture from Poggenpohl, a German kitchen and bathroom design firm. Cabinets, furniture, and appliances are built to make working in a kitchen efficient and without annoyance, to use space economically, and to provide the most aesthetically pleasing appearance under these conditions. It may seem like a difficult juggling act, but Poggenpohl succeeds at it, as demonstrated by Diagonale, its newest kitchen design (Series 2200). True to its name, this kitchen features most prominently the use of diagonal lines to an astonishing advantage. Corners in a kitchen, for example, have traditionally been dead space because box-shaped fixtures closed them out with harsh angles or overbearing, sweeping doors. The Diagonale kitchen has a tall unit in one corner, at a 45° angle with the wall, which makes use of all of the space there for storage with three carousel shelves inside a curved door. Thus, what used to serve no purpose provides the opportunity for one of the most important features of this kitchen.

Diagonal lines in design not only retrieve corners, but also join together areas of differing depths. An oven jutting out a yard from a row of cabinets would normally interfere with their doors and additional amounts of space. Poggenpohl adds a triangular cabinet space, not only providing more storage, but creating a continuity to the design which is much more handsome than either boxes springing out in different, shin-grabbing lengths, or a flat, impersonal wall of fixtures.

Another important feature of the kitchen is its work center. Poggenpohl tries to cluster as many major appliances together as possible within the constraints of individual designs. Shown here, for instance, is a low cooking area, counter top, and breakfast bar, all designed for comfortable, seated food preparation. The nasty hazard of banging one's head against an open cabinet door is reduced through these features of Poggenpohl's designs.

Quite a few appliances are incorporated intelligently into the Diagonale kitchen. Dishwashers, garbage bins, open shelving, and even electrical sockets blend in unobtrusively and yet functionally. The sink, shown here, is a notable example. It uses the diagonal style in two ways—it joins the small counter top with a larger working area and provides a niche into which someone using the sink can fit. The user is surrounded by the compartments of the sink, each at an easy reach. The Series 2200 sink also has a drainboard in the rear and is mounted flush with the counter top, eliminating the sink lip, often a dirt trap.

Also shown here is a cabinet with a rolling cover. This unit can store small electrical appliances, getting the little kitchen objects out of your way. The interior shelves can be adjusted in height, and electrical sockets are smoothly integrated into the design. The rolling cover remains in place at any required position.

The Diagonale kitchen comes in four styles—light oak front panels with hand-picked veneers, brown fumed oak front panels with hand-picked

veneers, patterned white laminate with solid beech rails on the top and bottom of panels, and jasmine-white laminate with solid beech rails on the top and bottom of panels.

For more information, contact:

Poggenpohl USA Corp.
6 Pearl Court
Allendale, NJ 07401
(201) 934-1511

MARAZZI

Ceramic tiles are the specialty of the world-wide Marazzi firm. In addition to materials brought in from Europe, the company manufactures ceramic tile in Texas. This facility and an extensive distribution system in place throughout North America make Marazzi's products especially useful options for the contemporary kitchen-dining area.

12½″ by 12½″ tiles are used in the combined cooking and dining space in the Albans Townhouse, Houston, Texas. Designed by William S. Stern & Associates, Architects, the room has an exceptionally neat, streamlined appearance. The softly glazed tile in the Milano color is from Marazzi's Metropoli Series and is offered as well in 6″ by 6″ and 8″ by 8″ sizes. There

are also 23 other handsome colors to choose from.

For information regarding the closest Marazzi distributor, contact:

Marazzi USA, Inc.
55 Clay and Scyene Rd.
Sunnyvale, TX 75182
(214) 226-0110

Kitchen Hardware and Fittings

If you think the fittings and hardware in a kitchen are unimportant little extras, just wait until your redwood cabinet doors fall off and the faucet on your all-important sink clogs up. With the selection of kitchen hardware as wide as it is today, it simply makes no sense to neglect such an important part of this room's design. With unusual new appliances and storage spaces on the market, the little extras are even more essential, since they must be specially adapted to unconventional circum-stances. Manufacturers of today's kitchen hardware have effectively rendered beautiful the design of these extremely functional objects, making the process of finding fittings quite painless.

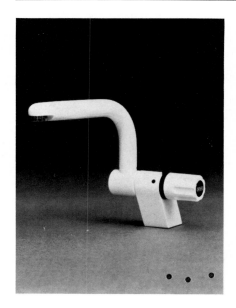

ABBAKA

Designed by Christian Bjørn and produced by CNB, both of Denmark, the Børmix 80 line of faucets imported by Abbaka combines unusual design with innovative plumbing. The valve used in the faucet shown here has a mechanism to adjust the maximum flow of water in order to conserve water. A lever controls the ratio of hot and cold water and thus eliminates the need for two-handled regulation. Børmix 80 is available in several modern designs for both the bathroom and the kitchen. It is made of solid-cast brass and comes in five enamel colors (blue, yellow, red, white, or brown) as well as a chrome finish.

For further information, contact:

Abbaka
435 23rd St.
San Francisco, CA 94107
(415) 648-7210

FORMS & SURFACES

This major American supplier of contemporary building materials has helped to transform the image of the architectural landscape from the mundane to the imaginative. Forms & Surfaces makes available the best in hardware designs from Europe and North America. If you appreciate the High Tech aesthetic, look no further for colorful, functional accessories for the bath or kitchen. Those shown here are of nylon, soft to the touch but extremely durable. Almost all the pieces are available in white, black, almond, gray, brown, red, yellow, green, blue, or orange.

A second line of Italian-designed cabinet pulls is made of die-cast metal, brass, black neoprene, and other synthetic materials. All the pulls

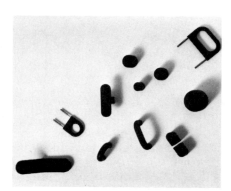

are offered in red, black, and white and several include polished chrome and bronze finishes as well.

For further information, contact:

Forms & Surfaces
Box 5215
Santa Barbara, CA 93108
(805) 969-7721

GROHE

Will wonders never cease? Throw away the old dish rag; banish Lola—the trusty German pots and pans brush—from the sink forever. Grohe offers a utensil set with a brush spray and a scraper spray that will attach right to a combination pull-out spray-hose/faucet of the Ladylux kitchen deck set. The design is superb and the choice of colors—white, mocha, beige, matte chrome, polished chrome, or red—will more than fill the bill. A single lever in the dual faucet/spray hose controls temperature and pressure. The handy brush and scraper come with their own mountable holder.

For further information, contact:

Grohe America, Inc.
2677 Coyle Ave.
Elk Grove Village, IL 60007
(312) 640-6650

HETTICH

If you find quality hardware for difficult-to-fit spaces almost impossible to find in retail outlets, Hettich America, a U.S. outpost for precisely

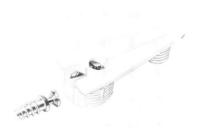

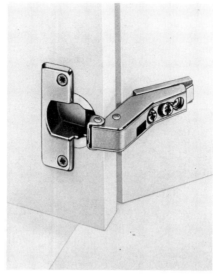

engineered German hardware, may be able to help you. All of its products are extremely durable. Illustrated are a two-piece fitting for right-angle joints which can be surface mounted and a concealed hinge for diagonal cabinets which does not require special side-panel mounting.

For further information, contact:

Hettich America Corp.
12428 Sam Neely Rd.
P.O. Box 7664
Charlotte, NC 28217
(704) 588-6666

KOHLER

Kohler, the leading manufacturer of plumbing fixtures in North America, offers hundreds of faucet designs from brass antique models to the most contemporary fixtures. The Finesse faucet is shown here. Resembling bees' wings, the handles are matched with a range of spouts from lavatory faucets to kitchen sink

faucets, depending upon your needs. Finesse faucets are made of solid brass and can be finished with either polished brass or chrome.

Kohler hardware is widely available in the United States and Canada. If you have difficulty in locating this particular fixture, contact:

Kohler Co.
Kohler, WI 53044
(414) 457-4441

Bath Designs and Essentials

The bathroom can be one of the most comfortable and attractive parts of the contemporary interior. The room has expanded from a simple, closet-like chamber to include vanities, ample cabinets, and dressing areas. Technologically, the modern bathroom has progressed as well, many boasting pulsating showerheads or saunas. While most bathrooms were once an antiseptic oasis of white tile and enamel, they now feature multi-colored tiles and hardware, fixtures in a wide variety of shades, and an assortment of handsome materials ranging from acrylic to marble.

POGGENPOHL

The bathroom designs created by Poggenpohl are rapidly becoming as well known and appreciated in North America as they are in Europe, the home base of the firm. The cabinet units, washbasins, and accessories combine practicality with a fine design sense. Materials are warm and inviting and of sturdy construction.

Poggenpohl's Softline cabinets and shelving are used in the first of the bathrooms illustrated. Shown is the ash veneer (FS 406) line; oak veneer and cherrywood veneer finishes are also offered. The washbasin counter top is constructed of one-piece Melamine in a planked ash finish. Two inset washbasins are set flush with

the surface. There are other Melamine finishes—blossom white, quartz, sand, and granite decor (a mottled brown composition)—that may be substituted for the planked ash. And edged basins which rest on the counter surface may be chosen rather than the flush units. Both of the basin types are available in thirteen different colors.

The second of the bathroom designs makes use of the Combi Soft (CS 120) line of white cabinets and shelving. The soft pink basin and counter top are special order items and are used here to show just how Poggenpohl cabinetry can be integrated with custom fixtures. The magnolia pink bow handles used for the cabinets are also from Poggenpohl. These are available in thirteen other colors as well. Round plastic knobs in eight different shades can also be specified.

Poggenpohl bath and kitchen designs are featured in kitchen and home centers across the United States and Canada. If information is not available in your area, contact:

Poggenpohl USA Corp.
6 Pearl Court
Allendale, NJ 07401
(201) 934-1511

TROMPLOY

A windowless bath can be one of the unpleasant realities of modern apartment life. Homeowners, too, sometimes face the same boxed-in situation when bathrooms have been tucked under stairways or in the space of an old dressing room. One

way out of this dilemma is to fake it, to create the illusion of an opening to the outside. Tromploy, a firm of artists who specialize in trompe l'oeil effects, provided a painted sky and the illusion of a neo-classical landscape for this otherwise drab bathroom in a New York City loft apartment. The murals are executed on canvas—as is most of the firm's work—and was easily mounted. Marbleizing floors and walls—another of the skills practiced by the two principals, Gary Finkel and Clyde Wachsberger—might also help to transform the utilitarian bath into something of considerably more interest and delight.

Tromploy works by commission and encourages inquiries.

For further information, contact:

Tromploy Studio and Gallery
400 Lafayette St., 5th Floor
New York, NY 10003
(212) 420-1639

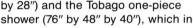

KOHLER

Anyone looking for modern bathroom fixtures should pay particular attention to Kohler's selection of products. As the leading manufacturer of plumbing fixtures in North America, Kohler can offer an enormous range and diversity of items from hot tubs to toilets. This graceful pedestal sink from Kohler, the Chardonnay model, features a curving

stand and a flaring basin. Measuring 28″ high and extending 21½″ from the wall, the sink has a 24″ by 15″ basin, 6″ deep. It is a medium-sized fixture compared with Kohler's other pedestal sinks, the LeGran and the Chablis. Made of vitreous china, the Chardonnay comes in black, gray, coffee, chocolate, taupe, raspberry, navy, white, rose, sand, parchment, almond, green, vanilla, and blue.

The stall shown here is one of the newest in Kohler's line of Perma-Wall Multi-Piece showers. The acrylic-like material allows for molded features such as the basic necessities of a built-in soap dish as well as flourishes that complement custom-designed bathrooms. Perma-Wall showers are also easy to install and clean, eliminating the need for tile or grout. The stall comes with a 36″-square base or a 36″ by 48″ base. They are available in nine shades—white, gray, rose, sand, parchment, almond, green, vanilla, and blue.

Most innovations in the design of showers have been mere modifications of the shower head. Kohler, however, has completely changed the experience of showering with the Swiss Shower, which has six single spout shower heads on its walls -- three in a vertical series on each side. A conventional shower head is also installed along with a diverter handle. The Swiss Shower comes in four models, including the medium-sized Trinidad one-piece shower (76″ by 36″ by 28″) and the Tobago one-piece shower (76″ by 48″ by 40″), which in-

cludes a corner seat and a sculpted toiletries ledge. Both models are made of fiberglass-reinforced acrylic and feature copper tubing. They are available in the same range of colors as the Perma-Wall units.

For further information, contact:

Kohler Co.
Kohler, WI 53044
(414) 457-4441

AMERICAN OLEAN

A tiled bath is the preference of almost every homeowner. It is easy to keep clean and has the tidy, streamlined look expected of such an interior. American Olean has been offering a wide selection of mosaic tiles for years, even when it appeared that ceramic products would be superseded by the use of synthetic materials. The handsome results achieved by use of a 4¼"-square antique-white textured tile from floor to ceiling is graphically illustrated in the first photo. The tile has been scored and grouted to suggest the use of even smaller squares.

2" by 2" dawn gray squares are used in the second illustration for flooring, to frame in the shower/tub, and to enclose the vanity.

American Olean tiles are found in many retail outlets. For further information regarding the products, contact:

American Olean Tile Co.
1000 Cannon Ave.
Landsdale, PA 19446-0271
(215) 855-1111

Lawrence Williams

Photographic Illustrations, Ltd.

VERMONT MARBLE

It is difficult to conceive of a material more appropriate for baths than marble. Few of us can afford the splendors of Caracalla, but a small investment in the real thing will pay dividends for years to come. Vermont Marble is one of the best and biggest suppliers of thin marble tile. This is not veneer, but ³⁄₈″-thick pieces available in custom dimensions or three modular sizes—12″ x 12″, 12″ x 5⁷⁄₈″, and 5⁷⁄₈″ x 5⁷⁄₈″. A wide range of colors is offered, from milky white to rich deep tones such as verde antique and Champlain black. "Timeless elegance" is a term best sparingly used. It does apply to a display of such incomparable stone.

For further information, contact:

Vermont Marble Co.
61 Main St.
Proctor, VT 05765
(802) 459-3311

Bath Hardware and Fittings

For the more modest bathroom in which luxurious fixtures are infeasible, the fittings are crucial to its design. Coordinated sets of faucets, towel racks, and other accessories can make the room luxuriously beautiful, especially considering the baked *enamel, chrome, brass, or even wood finishes available. In addition, original designs such as the Orchidea faucet shown in this section add imaginative form to color, possibly making the bathroom the most attractive room in the house.*

ABBAKA

Abbaka imports intelligently designed Danish bathroom fixtures, including the faucets and accessories presented here.

The prospect of turning off a regular faucet with greasy or soapy hands is a slippery one. The innovative design of the Børma-Handi faucet, however, solves the problem with lever handles that can be manipulated by just about anything apart from the usual forefinger and thumb—backs of hands, wrists, or even elbows. Those with disabilities or who are weak—the young, the old, the physically handicapped—will find the Børma-Handi especially valuable—the handles only require a quarter of a turn to shut them off tightly and are designed to be adjusted smoothly and easily. Børma-Handi faucets, available in designs for either the kitchen or bath, come plated in chromium.

Imported by Abbaka, Kosmos is a line of bathroom accessories designed by Christian Bjørn to complement Børma faucetry. Pictured here are six of the eleven pieces in this collection: clockwise from the top left, the Kosmos shelf, mirror holder, tumbler, toothbrush holder, toilet roll holder, and soap dish. These products are available in five enamel colors,—blue, yellow, red, white, and brown—in addition to a chrome finish. Kosmos fixtures, made of all brass, have mounting hardware which is concealed by "press-fit" cover caps, and are delivered ready to be installed.

For more information, contact:

Abbaka
435 23rd St.
San Francisco, CA 94107
(415) 648-7210

BALDWIN

Over a period of thirty-five years, Baldwin has built up a reputation as one of the finest American manufacturers of widely available bath accessories. Because of the hot forging process the company applies to its special brass alloy and the enamel coating baked on each item, Baldwin's fixtures are unusually durable. Two popular fixtures, a soap dish with bar (1) and a curved towel rack (2) complement all of the different Baldwin

lines of models. The soap dish measures 6½" long and extends 4½", while the towel bar is available in 16" and 24" lengths.

Baldwin Bath/Epic Accessories consist of a wide range of fixtures, including towel racks, bathrobe hooks, glass shelves, and towel rings in several elegant styles. The distinctive accessories all come with concealed mounting screws. Each model is available in several of Baldwin's finishes—polished or unpolished brass, polished or satin chrome, or a combination of polished brass and chrome. All of the towel ring models

shown here come with optional acrylic rods and rings.

Manhattan (3) is a smooth, tiered design. Dallas (4) has a simpler, bolder look of long knobs. Palm Springs (5), on the other hand, has a flat end for an attractively streamlined look. Atlanta (6), similar to the Manhattan model, is another tiered design.

For further information, contact:

Baldwin Hardware Corp.
841 Wyomissing Blvd.
Box 82
Reading, PA 19603

BRYAN PLASTICS

This Canadian firm specializes in well-wrought High-Tech plastic fixtures which are especially useful in the bath, although they may also be used in the kitchen and other areas of the house, depending on your taste. Since plastic is such a malleable medium, all of the objects are very streamlined in design. They include sinks, soap dishes, shelves and shelf supports, rails, pulls, and mirror frames. There is an excellent selection of colors to choose from, including yellow, green, red, gray, white, pink, purple, and brown.

For further information, contact:

Bryan Plastics Ltd.
8451 Dalton Rd.
Mount Royal, Quebec H4T 1V5
(514) 733-5341

CURVALINEAR

While brass and chrome are certainly good-looking in the bath, they can gleam a little too much for some. For these people, Curvalinear offers wooden bath fixtures, made of stained oak, lacquered to provide as much durability as metal fixtures. The shelves shown here (S18 and S23) are

18″ and 23″ long and 3¾″ wide, spacious enough to hold all sorts of supplies, but not deep enough to lose them in the rear. A 1⅞″-high slat of wood wraps around the clear acrylic base, serving as a guard rail to pre-

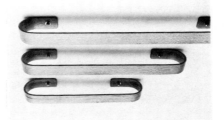

vent spills. The towel racks from Curvalinear shown here (T18, T23, and T28) have a similarly arched design. The slat shape of the rack frustrates attempts by towels to slip off. Available in lengths of 18″, 23″, and 28″, it is 1⅞″ thick and extends 3¾″.

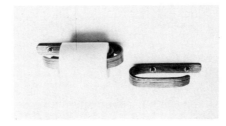

The paper holder, available in two styles, is a beautifully simple rack that eliminates the difficulties of spring-loaded dowels—the roll can slide on and then off. Without a dowel, the holder also does not allow the roll to unravel itself with one tug. The one-piece holder measures 8½″ long and 1¼″ thick and extends 3⅛″. The two-piece holder (shown with roll here) is 9½″ long and 1¼″ thick and extends 3⅞″.

For further information, contact:

Curvalinear
115 14th Ave. S.
Seattle, WA 98144
(206) 323-5471

GROHE

Plumbing fixtures are rather minor items in a decorating scheme, but objects which are not only durable but attractive only add to the value of your home and your living pleasure. Grohe of West Germany is an old firm with lots of up-to-date ideas which have finally reached North America.

Many of the Grohe fixtures are of solid

brass, as is the Roman Tub faucet set shown here. It is fitted out with brown onyx handles. The company's newest line of bath and kitchen fixtures is called "Harmony in White." All of the objects are of the sleek, sculpted design seen here in the basin set.

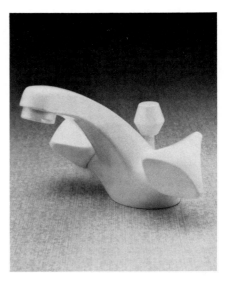

The Relaxa Champagne Shower System is also available in the gleaming white finish; both fixtures are of solid brass. The shower set is offered as well in polished chrome, polished brass, 23-karat gold, antique brass, pewter, and satin brass. There are various types of interchangeable shower heads that may be selected; it is easy to switch from one to another because of a snap-coupling mechanism. Leave it to the Germans to perfect such a useful system.

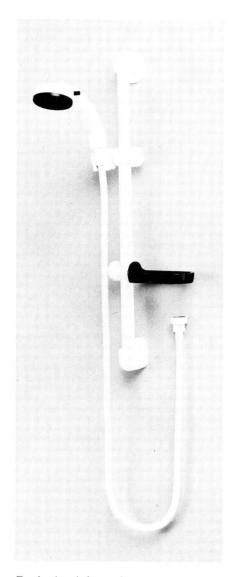

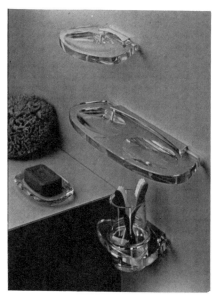

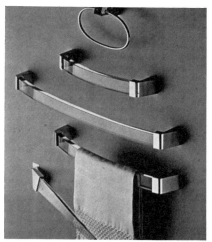

brass. Also available from the same designer are more conventionally formed towel rails of glass and brass.

For further information, contact:

Grohe America, Inc.
2677 Coyle Ave.
Elk Grove Village, IL 60007
(312) 640-6650

INTERNA DESIGNS

Bathroom hardware and fixtures from the Italian firm of Fontana Arte—available in the United States through Interna Designs—display all the slim elegance and fine finish associated with the best European craftsmanship.

The Celada series, named for designer Gianni Celada, includes several towel pegs or hooks in hand-beveled crystal glass and plated

Both types of accessories would bring to the bath not only an extra degree of convenience, but functional beauty as well. Fontana Arte's in-house designers are responsible for the sparkling crystal glass objects which compose the Classica series. Such mundane items as a soap dish and a toothbrush holder and glass are beautifully etched glass sculptures. The streamlined towel bars of crystal and chrome are not as imaginatively shaped, but

they are suitably durable for the intended use.

Color catalogue of bath and accessories, $20; color tear sheets mailed upon request.

Interna Designs, Ltd.
The Merchandise Mart
Space 6-168
Chicago, IL 60654
(312) 467-6076

KOHLER

Kohler offers one of the largest selections of bathroom hardware and fittings in North America. The sensuous curve of the firm's Cresent Spout is a pleasant alternative to the conventional straight arm of most faucets.

Shown here with Kohler's Alterna faucet handles, the Crescent Spout is available in brushed or polished chrome, brushed or polished 24-karat gold electroplate finish, or a polished-brass finish.

Also illustrated are a toilet paper holder and a double tumbler holder from the Bellamonté line of bathroom accessories from Kohler. Six other accessories are part of the series, made in Italy and finished with gold, polished chrome, or polished brass.

For further information, contact:

Kohler Co.
Kohler, WI 53044
(414) 457-4411

MIROIR BROT

Although Miroir Brot has been made in France since 1826, its boldly unadorned appearance makes it perfect for the contemporary bath.

The circular mirror magnifies its image three times its normal size and comes with a spotlight built into the mirror's surface that eliminates fogging while supplying strong light. The Miroir Brot can thus prove a loyal assistant to the meticulous shaver or make-up artist.

For further information, contact:

Miroir Brot, U.S.A.
5555 S. Sepulveda Blvd.

PAUL ASSOCIATES

Paul Associates produces an assortment of bathroom fixtures and accessories. Many of these products display a sophisticated use of rectangular shapes, such as the three lavatory basin sets shown here, all of which are designed by Stanley Paul.

The Pompton (1), an award-winning design, combines cylinders and thin blocks. With its tiered faucets and

handles, Aztec (2) has a somewhat Art Deco look, perfect for the '30s-inspired postmodern interior. The Argo

Culver City, CA 90230
(213) 204-4400

set (3) is more traditional, with a curved spout and rectangular handles. All of the lavatory sets are available in a brass or gold finish, or in a custom finish.

For more information, contact:

Paul Associates, Inc.
42-05 10th St.
Long Island City, NY 11101
(718) 784-2244

ROBERN

Robern offers six models of mirrored bathroom cabinets, including Swing Flect, shown here. The vinyl-backed mirror on this cabinet, ¼″ thick, will not shatter if broken, and so avoids the hazards of glass shards. The door turns on chrome pivot-pin hinges which will not, like conventional piano hinges, bind or wrack. The door also has built-in stresses so that it will remain in any given position and needs no magnetic catches. Made of anodized aluminum, the Swing Flect comes in a range of sizes. Robern will also make custom-sized cabinets upon request.

For more information, contact:

Robern Inc.
1670 Winchester Rd.
Bensalem, PA 19020
(215) 245-6550

WATERCOLORS

The Europeans are unquestionably ahead of us when it comes to bathroom fixtures. While American designers are just discovering the possibilities of nontraditional, curved faucetry, European manufacturers are producing avant-garde, asymmetrical fixtures. Watercolors, an importer of Italian designs, offers impressive testimony to the European supremacy.

The Orchidea stands out among generally unimaginative fixtures as a truly well-sculpted faucet. Using a curved spout and a single-lever handle, two ordinary faucet elements, Zazzeri S.A.S. of Italy creates a plant-like object that seems to supply water as a botanical function. Available in

several enamel colors as well as brass or chrome, the Orchidea faucet is part of a full line of fixtures for the tub, kitchen, shower, or bar.

Especially attractive are the objects which make up the Tubotondo series. Shown is a towel hook and a towel bar of steel tubing finished in baked yellow enamel. There are seven other colors available to fit almost any decorating scheme, as well as polished chrome, brass, and gold. Other accessories such as a towel bar, glass holder, soap holder, paper holder, and several sizes of shelves are also offered.

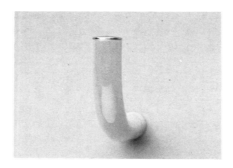

For further information, contact:

Watercolors Inc.
Garrison, NY 10524
(914) 424-3327

Other Suppliers of Kitchen and Bath Designs and Hardware

Consult List of Suppliers for addresses.

Kitchen Designs and Appliances

Allmilo Corp.
ARD Custom Kitchens and Baths
Atag USA Corp.
Elkay Mfg. Co.
Fresh Impressions
International Contract Furnishers
   Inc. (ICF)
Jenn-Air Corp.
St. Charles Manufacturing Co.
Siematic
Wall-Goldfinger

Kitchen Hardware and Fittings

ARD Custom Kitchens and Baths
Classic Moulders
Eljer Plumbingware
Grohe America Inc.
Plexability
Waterworks

Bath Designs and Essentials

Amaru Tile International
Amerec Corporation
American Marble & Flooring Co.
ARD Custom Kitchens and Baths
Caracalla Contemporary Baths Ltd.
Elon, Inc.
P. E. Guerin Inc.
Hastings Tile & Il Bagno Collection
Kirsch Co.
William Lyons Design Craft, Inc.
Sherle Wagner International

Bath Hardware and Fittings

ARD Custom Kitchens and Baths
Artistic Brass
Classic Moulders
Decorative Hardware Studio
Eljer Plumbingware
Plexability
Smolka

American Olean Tiles kitchen design
with ebony and white porcelain tiles.

4.

Decorative Finishes

Under the general heading of decorative finishes are found various materials used to add color, pattern, and texture to contemporary design—fabrics, ceramic tiles, rugs, carpeting, laminates, papers, and shades. They are, essentially, the clothes a room wears. The interaction between such materials and a room is also like that between clothes and a person: they define an image and, to do so effectively, must be well-coordinated.

In order to define the modern image, designers in the 1920s and '30s declared representational images outdated, branding prints of flowers, birds, and Greek vases old-fashioned. Contemporary patterns continue to reach abstraction, but not so solemnly as in the past. Exaggerating and juxtaposing natural, everyday images, designers have created disconcerting, even surreal appearances. Ceramicists offer tiles with abstract designs as well, combining them with textures and glazes that are very natural.

The various decorative finishes in this chapter complement the furniture and overall design of a room, and they have an intrinsic beauty as well. They are deliberately obtrusive, capturing one's eye with luxuriant patterns ranging from chaotic geometrics on rugs to swirling marbling on papers. So removed from the stern, whitewashed walls of the International era, these patterns and textures exemplify the warm liveliness that is a welcome feature of postmodernism.

Sunar-Hauserman fabrics designed by Jacqueline Johnson and Merle Barnett —from top to bottom, Hamilton, Roberson, Desmond, Browning, and Rothschild.

Defining a new style of design requires reviving the older motifs that complement it; the Victorians, for example, found that the Gothic style suited their tastes quite well, both morally and aesthetically. Presently, the ancient techniques of ikat and batik are popular for fabrics and textiles, giving modern abstract motifs vigor and luxury. These styles accommodate other contemporary fabrics with newer patterns, such as computer blips and New Wave spatterings, making the selection of modern textiles an eclectic range of exciting patterns.

ALGEMENE FLUWELLWEVERIJ

The contemporary upholstery textiles created by Algemene Fluwellweverij in Belgium are works of art. The design of these woven fabrics of 100% cotton is without peer. Yet these are commercial products and not one-of-a-kind creations. The patterns, bold and generally geometric, are woven in a manner which accentuates the play of color and composition. Illustrated is the Cupido pattern, a heavy, textured fabric that is of timeless elegance. This and other designs unique to the manufacturer have won countless design awards.

For further information, contact the company's U.S. agent:

*V. Guttmann Corp.
95 Madison Ave.
New York, NY 10016
(212) 689-1899*

BRUNSCHWIG & FILS

Brunschwig & Fils' Docu-Drama collection of fabrics demonstrates the firm's wide-ranging array of styles. Kabul features a warp print from the Ikat style of resist-dyeing the warp before weaving, which makes Kabul far richer and dependable than warp prints simply applied to the woven fabric. Made of pure silk in Korea, the fabric is available in six color combinations, including terra cotta and wine, and is 47″ wide.

The checks and blips on Watson Woven Texture, here used as upholstery material, come from the modern computer image and are arranged in eight different color combinations, including shades of gray and white and beige and white, to make an attractive pattern. Watson Woven Texture is made of 59% cotton and 41% viscose and is available in 52"-wide rolls.

For further information, contact:

Brunschwig & Fils, Inc.
979 Third Ave.
New York, NY 10022
(212) 838-7878

CARLETON V

Carleton V infuses its fabric, Celebration, with a powerful, elegant simplicity. Handloomed in an Ikat pattern in India, the all-silk fabric makes for beautiful draperies and upholstery material. Carleton V weaves Celebration 48" wide with a 20" repeat, in a choice of four color combinations.

For further information, contact:

Carleton V
979 Third Ave.
New York, NY 10022
(212) 355-4525

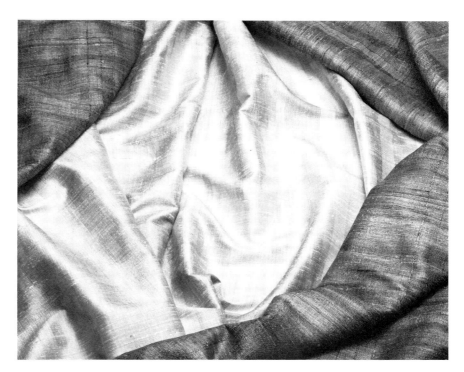

YVES GONNET

The three musketeers of Dumas' romance—Porthos, Athos, and Aramis—lend their names to these fabrics made by Yves Gonnet and illustrated here. True to their namesakes, these geometric chintzes are appropriately bold. One is a houndstooth pattern, which combines with stripes in a second to form squares. A coordinating third fabric is also available, consisting of the houndstooth and stripes in alternating columns. The designs are available in four color combinations, ranging from brown and burgundy to gray and tan. All of the fabrics are 100% cotton and made in 56″-wide rolls.

For further information, contact:

Yves Gonnet, Inc.
979 Third Ave.
New York, NY 10022
(212) 758-8220

have come from the design studio of Anni Albers. Each fabric is 100% cotton and offered in the combination shown and in seven other color schemes.

Dialogue is a straightforward 100% cotton architectural print in five color combinations produced by Waverly, a Schumacher subsidiary. Pick Up Sticks might well have been designed by a member of the Memphis group. Its turquoise shade and overall funky design are reminiscent of the 1950s. There are also three other color combinations.

If information on these and other Schumacher or Waverly fabrics is not available locally, contact:

Schumacher
939 Third Ave.
New York, NY 10022
(212) 644-5900

L.E. CARPENTER

SCHUMACHER

Schumacher, one of America's leading quality textile and wallpaper firms, has thousands of designs available for the professional or home decorator. Many of these can be found in home centers, fabric shops, and paint and paper stores. This accessibility makes their stylish fabrics doubly attractive. Included among those especially appropriate for contemporary interiors is the sampling shown clockwise from

right: Madsden Check, Coach, Midland Plaid, Dialogue, and Pick Up Sticks.

The three woven fabrics are appropriate for upholstery, Madsden Check, resembling a modern quilt design, is available in the colors shown and in eight other color combinations and is part nylon, part wool. Both Coach and Midland Plaid could

Textured fabrics can provide a softening touch in a starkly modern architectural setting. Carpenter, a manufacturer best known for vinyl wallcoverings, has just introduced the Softech collection for office use; it is also appropriate for many residential interiors. All of the fabrics are made of wool, wool/polyester, or wool-silk combinations. Among the fifteen rich tweed weaves are designs appropriate for use as wallcoverings, draperies, or upholstery. The fabrics shown here, from top to bottom, are Greenwich, suggested as a wallcovering; Waterford, suitable to be hung at the windows; and Hampshire, for upholstered furniture. There are many soft colors to choose from.

For further information, contact:

L.E. Carpenter & Co.
170 N. Main St.
Wharton, NJ 07885
(201) 366-2020

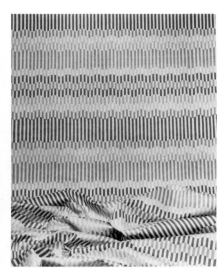

CHINA SEAS

Over the years, China Seas has produced a number of types of batiks, but by its own admission, Bunga, its first design (shown here), remains one of its most popular. The bright colors and strong patterns of this batik, a convention in Indonesia where it was designed, is finding a new home among admirers of contemporary design. Bunga is made of cotton and is 40″ wide. It is available in green, black, and beige. China Seas also makes wallcoverings and screen prints.

For more information, contact:

China Seas, Inc.
21 E. 4th St.
New York, NY 10003
(212) 420-1170

DESCHEMAKER

Acapulco, illustrated here, is one of several new fabrics made by Deschemaker, Inc. The multi-colored quilted squares create a pleasant pattern that can be used for many purposes. The fabric (51% nylon, 34% cotton, and 15% viscose) comes in six lively color combinations and in widths of 55″. Deschemaker is a leading French fabric manufacturer and has opened its first American showroom in New York's Design & Decoration Building.

Those interested in products from Deschemaker should note that they are available through designers, architects, and specifiers.

For more information, contact:

Deschemaker, Inc.
979 Third Ave.
New York, NY 10022
(212) 319-5730

FIRST EDITIONS

First Editions, headquartered in New York, produces contemporary screen-printed wallcoverings and fabrics. As these two examples demonstrate, First Editions has found that being "contemporary" can actually mean, stylistically, quite a few different things. Billy Joe, shown here, is a complex combination of patterned waves of color in horizontal bands of vertical stripes. In plain contrast to this subtle yet mesmerising design is Deschamps, also

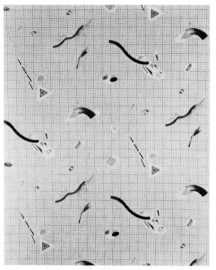

shown here. Jagged motifs thrown randomly on a stark grid form a playful pattern with a 36″ repeat. Both styles come in wallcoverings and matching polished cotton fabric. They are available in widths of 48″ and in a number of stock custom color combinations.

Prints from First Editions are available through designers, architects, and specifiers.

For further information, contact:

First Editions Wallcoverings and
**   Fabrics, Inc.**
979 Third Ave.
New York, NY 10022
(212) 355-1150

GROUNDWORKS

Contemporary interiors often require little in the way of draperies or curtains. The play of light through large expanses of glass is to be enjoyed

Roger Bester

and the outdoors invited in. Lightweight textiles in soft colors may provide just the right amount of filtered sunlight, and a modicum of privacy day and night. Groundworks' Modern Sheers collection is designed for this purpose. The gossamer fabrics—of nylon, linen, wool, silk, Trevira, and polyester—are available in widths ranging from 34″ to 120″.

For further information, contact:

Groundworks
231 E. 58th St.
New York, NY 10022
(212) 759-8250

KIRK-BRUMMEL

More than just contemporary fabrics, several new designs by Kirk-Brummel pay homage to the influences that have helped form the contemporary sensibility itself. Two fabrics are inspired by Josef Hoffmann and are entitled "Hoffmann" (left and right) and "Hoffmann Check" (center). (In 1903 Hoffmann founded the Wiener Werkstätte, the famous design cult that developed several innovations in decoration.) The assembly of different geometrical elements creates a vivacious effect in this fabric. These designs (58% viscose, 35% cotton, and 7% polyester) are available in widths of 51″.

Paul Klee, whose use of line made his artwork unmistakable, inspires Kirk-Brummel's design, Klee. Areas of different shades and color values, together with subtle weaving effects, suggest the master's technique. The fabric, imported from France, is a blend of wool, cotton, and polyester, and is available in a 50″ width.

Designs fundamental to the beginnings of modern architecture are found in Bauhaus. Based on the style promoted by the world-famous German school, c.1920, the design of this fabric depends on sleek curves and superpositions of mechanical lines. Bauhaus comes in two color combinations of teal and rust. Made of 75% cotton and 25% viscose, the fabric is 52″ wide with a 14″ repeat.

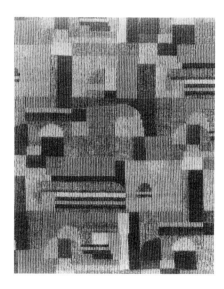

Reflecting the more anonymous, but ubiquitous, effects of the computer on the modern age is PC Junior, a series of four patterns of easily recognizable computer blips and images. The designs (from left to right, Wang, McIntosh, Apple, and PC Junior) come in four different color combinations and all complement each other. Imported from Holland, these fabrics are 100% wool and 55″ wide.

For more information, contact:

Kirk-Brummel Associates, Inc.
979 Third Ave.
New York, NY 10022
(212) 477-8590

LEE/JOFA

What happens when a century-old fabric firm uses millenia-old Incan motifs? A contemporary design is created, of course. The three patterns shown here are designed by Edith de Lisle and manufactured by Lee/Jofa. Chimu Print (left) is a pattern of differently colored birds in a 23¼″ repeat. Paracas Print (center) depicts the Incan god with a 23⅝″ repeat. And Mariana Coordinating Print (right), with a 7″ repeat, serves to unite the entire collection. Four colors are available for these fabrics—peach, ivory, rust, and stone—along with a distinctive metallic-gold screen. These designs are 48″ wide and made of 100% cotton. In addition to the Gold of Peru series, Lee/Jofa makes a variety of fabrics, ranging from conventional floral prints to bright pastel patterns.

For more information, contact:

Lee/Jofa
800 Central Blvd.
Carlstadt, NJ 07072
(201) 438-8444

KATHERINE RADCLIFFE

The process of making marbled paper has not changed significantly since its invention in the late Middle Ages, nor has its hypnotic appeal ever diminished. Confined for a period to the inside of book covers, the marbling process has spread recently to a number of uses, including the decoration of cloth. Marbling, formed by the random movement of fluids, demonstrates perhaps more than any other craft the limitless range of artistic expression. Katherine Radcliffe, a practitioner of the art for more than a decade, offers wall coverings, silk scarves, and even jewelry with the magically liquid decoration. Her work has been sold through Louis W. Bowen of New York and the Metropolitan Museum of Art.

For further information, contact:

Katherine Radcliffe
7 Jane Street
New York, NY 10014
(212) 691-4697

SUNAR-HAUSERMAN FABRICS

Sunar-Hauserman recognizes the present demand from designers and consumers for livelier, richer patterns in fabrics. "In the early days of the modern movement," explains a company spokesman, "the demands were for fabrics really with no interest. But today we are turning away from that bland nonstatement to new richness and sparkle in patterns, weaves, and textures." Jacqueline Johnson and Merle Barnett, partners in Johnson Barnett, Inc., of New York have therefore designed these woven upholstery fabrics for Sunar-Hauserman. Shown here are several designs from the collection—from top to bottom, Hamilton, Roberson, Desmond, Browning, and Rothschild. The patterns on other designs range from strongly geometric ones to those casually speckled. The fabrics vary widely in color, texture, and materials as well: the collec-

tion includes fabrics made of wool, cotton, velvet, and leather.

For further information, contact:

Sunar-Hauserman
5711 Grant Ave.
Cleveland, OH 44105
(216) 883-1400

WOODSON

Wazato is a departure for Woodson, well known for its floral print fabrics. Designed by Joyce Vaiser, the series of seven patterns of fabric takes as inspiration the Japanese tradition of geometric design. Made of pure cotton, the fabrics are available in three color combinations: red, green, and purple on black; beige, green, and gray on dark green; and rose, lavender, and mint on gray. Genki is a diamond-shaped pattern with superimposed waving stripes; Hishi consists of larger diamonds with small detailing. Kotos is a houndstooth design, and Myabi is a sparse paisley

pattern. The broad stripes on Asuka are intersected by diagonal stripes, while on Koshi they form a plaid crisscrossed by thin lines set perpendicularly. Their bold geometric patterns make them excellent choices for curtains and slip covers in a contemporary home. Genki and Jima also come in wallcoverings.

For further information, contact:

Woodson
200 Lexington Ave.
New York, NY 10016
(212) 684-0330

Ceramics

The selection of poorly designed, poorly made tiles at the local outlet store should not scare you away from ceramics in general. Individual craftsmen have transformed tiles and other forms of ceramics into such extraordinary pieces of art that their works may be *wall-hung in and for themselves. Some use repeating patterns on a grid of tiles, while others use single slabs of clay. In any case, they are eye-catching alternatives to flat paintings or fuzzy wall-hangings as ways to decorate walls anywhere in the house.*

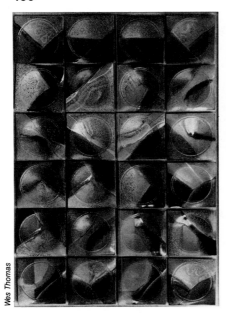

Wes Thomas

FARRELL PORCELAIN

One of the challenges in making a repeating pattern of wall tiles is to avoid a monotonous grid of identical units. In Waving Quilt, Richard and Sandra Farrell have created a series of twenty-four impressed tiles, but allow a looseness in the design by placing the tiles slightly askew. Each tile is also uniquely glazed with several layers of color to counter the regularity as well. The 32″-wide, 48″-high piece is colored with purple and celadon.

For further information, contact:

Farrell Porcelain
P.O. Box 108
East Killingly, CT 06243
(203) 774-8967

STARBUCK GOLDNER

It often seems that tiles must either be practical or artistic, but Starbuck Goldner Studios demonstrates how they can be both. The artisans mass produce their tiles to be able to take heavy use, but the repeating patterns on the tiles are designed to derive beauty from the same repetition. The Double Curves style shown here, consisting of turquoise glazed tiles, each 5¾″ square, attracts the eye first to the major pattern of waving lines and

then to the specific design on each tile. Starbuck Goldner Studios makes tiles in every shape from triangles to trapeziums, with a geometric agility one associates with Islamic designs. The tiles come in two types: either flat tiles, intended for any surface including walkways, hearths, and counters; or relief tiles such as Double Curves, suited to areas of lighter use such as walls and borders. The studio specializes in custom work as well as antique tile restoration.

For further information, contact:

Starbuck Goldner Studios
315 W. Fourth St.
Bethlehem, PA 18015
(215) 866-6321

George Erml

DOROTHY HAFNER

Dorothy Hafner gives her work in porcelain dinnerware and architectural tiles a dynamism that is distinctively her own. Key West, a design of architectural tiles, sets white against black, with jumbled and energetic angles and spots interspersed throughout. The hand-painted tiles measure 6″ square and are suitable as floor or wall decorations.

For further information, contact:

Dorothy Hafner

44 Cooper Square, #3R
New York, NY 10003
(212) 677-9797

Victor Krispin

PHILIP JAMESON

Philip Jameson finds order in incongruity with his ceramic artwork. Ceramics are generally made as vessels or bowls that sit on a pedestal, but Jameson only makes hanging works that seem to spring off a wall. To involve the wall even further in his works, he does not make conventional solid ceramic objects, but ones with gaps for the wall to peek through. The textures on Points of New Interest, shown here, are typical of Jameson's delightfully hodge-podge style. Coils, disks, ridges, and even a human face are jumbled together. Unlike other ceramicists, Jameson uses bright acrylic paints instead of grainy organic colors. The result is initially explosive, but the piece invites the viewer to consider it closely, to establish a meaning for it and discover the underlying composition. This work, made of clay with gesso, measures 28″ high, 24″ wide, and 1″ deep.

For further information, contact:

Philip Jameson
Sonoma State University
Department of Art
Rohnert Park, CA 94978
(707) 664-2151

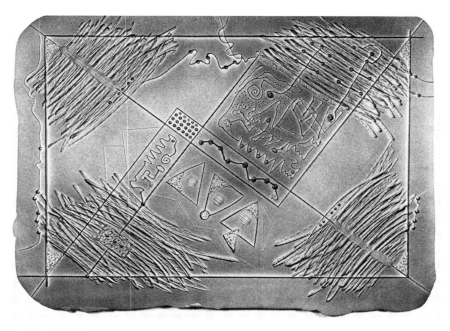

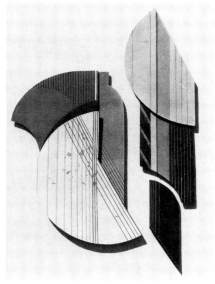

JERE LYKINS

Throughout his career, Jere Lykins has continually perfected his unique style of ceramics-making. He began making ceramic reliefs with the Japanese Raku method, using depth extensively but not coloring his work to a great extent. Moving to an electric kiln and then acrylic paints, Lykins has come to rely more heavily on brighter colors. His use of dimensional relief has become so subtle that he uses 1/4"-thick clay slabs with thin grooves. Typical of Lykins's recent works is the wall relief shown here. The entire piece, framed and protected by plexiglass, measures 23½" by 29" by 1".

For further information, contact:

Jere Lykins
P.O. Box 580
Mt. Berry, GA 30149
(404) 232-5374

elements such as disks, shards, and columns into an integral design. For this porcelain wall relief, Otis uses colored clay and slips. It measures 47" by 32" by 1½".

For further information, contact:

Jeanne Otis
The Hand and Spirit Crafts Gallery
4222 N. Marshall Way
Scottsdale, AZ 85251
(602) 946-4529

ELIZABETH MACDONALD

Some of Elizabeth MacDonald's ceramic murals are like faded mosaics unearthed from a buried temple, depicting landscapes, skies, and, shown here, an old barn. MacDonald tears the edges of the small, rough tiles she uses for her distinctive murals. When they are still damp, she paints them with colored slips, and after they are fired she assembles the tiles on a wooden substructure. The result is a soft, geological scheme of colors on a seemingly worn surface. This 48"-square work demonstrates how her juxtaposition of fields of colors, subdued in themselves, creates a dramatic scene.

Information packet and slides, $15.

Elizabeth MacDonald
Box 205
Bridgewater, CT 06752
(203) 354-0594

JEANNE OTIS

The etched lines Jeanne Otis makes with an underglaze pencil create a sophisticated effect on her ceramic tiles. By making these grooves on such works as Nightwalker, Nighttalker, shown here, she joins together

ROBERT SPERRY

Robert Sperry, a veteran of decades of ceramic tile work, has developed a style that is at once fluid and monumental. He does not know quite what will emerge from his kiln, since he deliberately eschews safe finishes. Using white clay slip on 16"-square black tiles, Sperry allows a high temperature fire to crack, melt, and pop his swirls.

Sperry is pictured here before his Untitled #625, a mural of 176 tiles which

Roger Schreiber

stretches across thirty feet of the Kings County Administration Building in Seattle. This work combines several styles of slip—geometric shapes with sharp borders, patches of irregular, blistered clay, and fainter clouds in the background. While Sperry's work is on a scale too large for the average home, it is spectacular for commercial buildings.

For further information, contact:

Robert Sperry
120 E. Edgar St.
Seattle, WA 98102
(206) 242-8688

WHITEHEAD STUDIOS

Tiles can serve a number of purposes in design: small repeating patterns create a subdued background for a room, while tile murals are a bold form of trompe l'oeil which reduces the tile to merely a durable canvas.

Whitehead Studios explores the full range of these artistic possibilities with custom ceramic tile patterns ranging from barnyard animals to this French country kitchen scene. All Whitehead tiles measure either $4\frac{1}{4}$"- or 6"-square, and an extensive stock of ceramic glazes from which to choose is maintained.

For more information, contact:

Whitehead Studios
The Merchandise Mart
Suite 1234-A
Chicago, IL 60654
(312) 661-1494

Floor Coverings

The design in rugs and carpets tends now towards the energetic and ornamental. Handwoven rugs with quilt-like patterns and traditional methods of weaving warm the floors once laid bare by minimalist designs. Wall-to-wall synthetic carpeting is still available for the office, but it, too, has found character and spirit where before there was only a vast, patternless expanse. An element of design too often neglected in recent years, the floor covering is proving once again to be a beautiful addition to contemporary design.

AMS IMPORTERS

Although the designers of Rollakan area carpets strive to preserve the traditional spirit of the Swedish province of Skane in their products, these carpets blend into contemporary environments quite well. Shown here are Design #124 and Scandia, two examples of geometric patterns that the makers of Rollakan carpets emphasize. These carpets are meticulously well-made. Handwoven completely with wool (with an all-cotton warp),

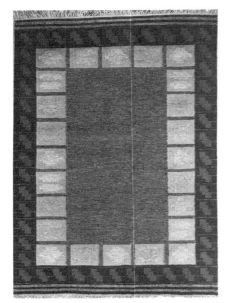

they are flatwoven and thus reversible. A sign of quality is the artist's initials which are woven into each rug. Rollakan carpets now come in eight designs, most of which can be purchased in four colors—blue, brown, green, and rose. AMS Importers are the sole importers of Rollakan rugs in the United States.

For further information, contact:

AMS Importers
23 Ash Lane
Amherst, MA 01002
(413) 253-2644

BIGELOW-SANFORD

Times Square is a departure from conventional, bland designs in wall-to-wall carpeting intended for offices. The pattern is as suitable for residential use, especially in heavy traffic areas, as for a sophisticated commercial space. The carpeting is dyed so that the color design penetrates to the

back of the material. Times Square is one of Bigelow-Sanford's New Beauvais patterns, a series of printed cut-pile carpets made of two-ply Anso X nylon and available in nine small-, mid-, and large-scale patterns. There are five different color combinations to select from in each of the patterns.

STANLEY BULBACH

"Handmade" seems almost an understatement when describing Stanley Bulbach's rugs. He spins his own yarn from Lincoln and Romney wools and colors it himself with natural dyes. In using some dyes, such as indigo, Bulbach must dip his rugs as many as thirty-six times to achieve the desired tint. He has explored weaving techniques extensively and has settled on a combination of a Navajo vertical loom and Moroccan methods of weaving. Following this North African process, he retains a long fringe at the top of his rugs, which he knots ornamentally. Bulbach has created three categories for his rugs—flying, bed, and prayer. He assures us that his flying carpets are permanently grounded, but their energetic repeating patterns do give them a sensation of movement. Azaleas in Rain, shown here, is a flying carpet made of black Lincoln wool and is dyed with cochineal. It measures 3' by 6'.

For more information about the New Beauvais line, contact:

Bigelow-Sanford Inc.
Box 3089
Greenville, SC 29602
(803) 299-2000

Bed carpets have dreamier patterns and are softer than flying carpets while prayer carpets have designs which create a focal point for sitting and are made of fibered wool spun with a hard twist. Halloween, for example, is a prayer carpet with patterns

Indi 500 is a series of flags against a gray background. Given its tension between checkered squares and solid colors, the rug has a feeling of movement appropriate to its name.

The small touches of color in Two Gray Hills emphasize the depths of the gray rectangles that dominate the rug's pattern. White and black, made part of the jumble of blocks, seem also to become shades of gray in this optically opulent rug.

Pick Up Sticks sets brightly colored tufted streaks diagonally against a bland, flat, striped background. The result is a playful combination that draws the eye of the viewer into a complex network of lines and colors.

T-Waves demonstrates Cress's skill of transforming blocks of color—a rainbow of T-shaped rectangles are set in

in goldenrod and indigo. Measuring 3′ by 6′, it is woven from a combination of brown Romney crossbreed wools.

For further information, contact:

Stanley Bulbach
239 W. 15th St.
New York, NY 10011
(212) 243-9010

DAVID CRESS

In his rugs and tapestries, David Cress experiments with blocks of color, creating energetic designs with squares and rectangles. Shown here are four of his tufted rugs made of 100% wool.

sloping rows of gray blocks. The vibrant design has the same power one would expect from a curving pattern.

All of Cress's rugs are available in three sizes—3' by 5', 4' by 6' 8", and 6' by 10'.

For further information, contact:

David Cress
274 N. Goodman St.
Rochester, NY 14607
(716) 442-9657

Cress's works can also be purchased through:

Rosanne Raab Associates
60 Franklin Rd.
Scarsdale, NY 10583
(914) 472-8788

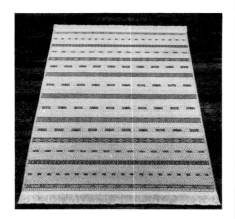

EUROTEX

Eurotex offers a wide range of natural and synthetic floor and wall coverings. Marrakesh #1200, shown here, is one of a new series of rugs made by Eurotex. It is an all-wool rug from Spain and is available in three sizes. Marrakesh #1200 comes only in white with blue and orange details.

For more information, contact:

Eurotex
165 W. Ontario St.
Philadelphia, PA 19140
(215) 739-8844

INTERFACE FLOORING SYSTEMS

Advances in carpet technology have been a mixed blessing. "Progress" has provided us with indoor-outdoor carpeting, most often a lightweight, questionable synthetic weave (Is it mouse hair? Crushed bat wings?) of a sickly hue. It wears quickly and, if touched with moisture, never seems to dry out. Indoor-outdoor carpeting is best reserved for locker rooms. Yet there are durable weaves of considerable appeal which are used in many sophisticated commercial settings and are just as appropriate for residential use. Interface's Graphic Innovations line of carpet tiles is such a well-designed, well-produced carpet collection.

As illustrated, there are 16 patterns available in the 18"-square modules.

Available in a cut-pile or loop-pile 100%-nylon finish, squares such as these have a great advantage over continuous broadloom: They can be replaced easily. Their use in bathrooms, front halls, and playrooms is especially to be recommended. Each square is backed with five layers of vinyl and fiberglass. Most of the tiles can be free-laid; some require gluing.

Although intended primarily for use in offices or commercial establishments, Graphic Innovations carpet tile designs are well-conceived, and the color selection gratifying. There are eight shades to choose from, among them iced plum, bristol blue, and dusty rose. Patterns can be mixed and matched so as to create borders, centerpieces, or free-form designs.

For further information, contact:

Interface Flooring Systems, Inc.
P.O. Box 1503, Orchard Hill Rd.
LaGrange, GA 30241
(404) 882-1891

In Canada:

Interface Flooring Systems
(Canada), Inc.
Marketing Group
P.O. Box 1182
Belleville, ONT K8N 5E8
(613) 966-8090

STARK CARPET

Stark offers Diagonal Twill, an award-winning carpet with a soft, striped pattern. It is hand-woven and all wool, with a reversible twill weave and a fringed border. Diagonal Twill is available in several sizes, and is available through designers, architects, and specifiers. Stark offers a large assortment of other carpeting as well.

For further information, contact:

Stark Carpet Corp.
979 Third Ave.
New York, NY 10022
(212) 752-9000

CHRISTINE VAN DER HURD

Christine Van der Hurd offsets the strength and severity of Present Mood, her limited edition of rugs, with cheerful colors. The large triangles and squares are set against a series of stripes and sprinkled with dots, and Van der Hurd has selected mauve, chrome, yellow, aqua, gray, and ultramarine to define the shapes. Hand-tufted, these plush rugs are made entirely of wool with flat dense piles. The five styles in the collection are available in sizes ranging from 3'6" by 7'6" to 6' by 9'.

For further information, contact:

Modern Age Galleries
795 Broadway
New York, NY 10003
(212) 674-5603

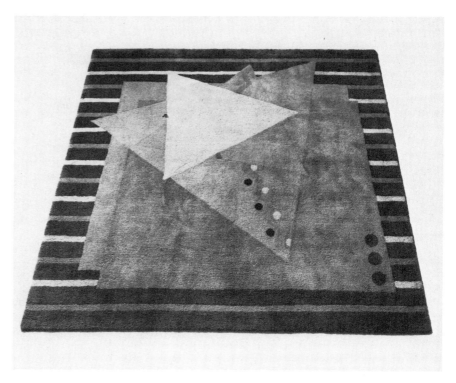

Laminates

Because laminates are readily available in building supply stores, the consumer does not generally need the help of a source book to find various brands. Laminates are making their way into homes as a counter-top and wallcovering material in bathrooms and kitchens. The possibilities of laminates in design are only just being explored in substances like Colorcore from Formica, a material in which the color extends throughout and not just on the surface. Colorcore can be easily shaped to interesting forms. Presented here is also another unusual laminate, suitable for any part of the contemporary home.

FORMS & SURFACES

Color-Walls and Metal-Walls, made by Lamin-Art, Inc., and sold by Forms & Surfaces, provide the freedom and flexibility a designer demands. Color-Walls, for example, consist of plastic laminates backed with tempered hardboard and can be used on walls, columns, ceilings, and counter faces. Color-Walls are made in a range of thicknesses and colors; they are also available with 2"-wide strips of laminate alternating with 1"-wide strips of plexiglass. Similar to Color-Walls, Metal-Walls are made with metal laminates. Both materials can also be applied to curved surfaces.

For further information, contact:

Forms & Surfaces
Box 5215
Santa Barbara, CA 93108
(805) 969-7721

Papers

Wallpaper's former supremacy as a wallcovering is being eroded by other types of decoration, such as tiles, woven wall hangings, and trompe-l'oeil painting. Once the basic element of wall decoration, wallpaper now seems often dull and passé. It can only remain viable in contemporary design if designers come up with more imaginative styles than lots of little blue flowers. Here are two examples of what can be done.

IMPERIAL WALLCOVERINGS

Lines that seem almost scribbled create a vivaciousness appropriate to this wallpaper's name—Summer Garden. Imperial Wallcoverings offers this and 118 other designs in Style, a collection which the firm describes as "Lifestyle Decorating." These patterns come in a range of shades and coordinating borders and fabrics. The sidewalls are pre-pasted and can be scrubbed clean; the accompanying

fabrics are printed in 45"- or 54"-wide rolls.

For further information, contact:

Imperial Wallcoverings, Collins & Aikman Corp.

23645 Mercantile Rd.
Cleveland, OH 44122
(216) 464-3700

Shades and Blinds

Shades and blinds have long been used simply to keep out glare and onlookers, but now some are being treated to retain and dissipate heat economically. Blinds are also coming into their own in design; with attractive hardwood slats and brightly colored canvas, they can be surprisingly beautiful, even overpowering other features of a room. The potentiality of these fields of horizontal and vertical lines in design has hardly yet been realized.

CASTEC

The adaptability of Canvas Pacifica folding shades make them quite useful in contemporary interior design. They are unobtrusive both when in use or when folded away, and can be hooked to a motor-driven shade operator. Castec, which makes these shades, offers them in over ten different colors or will make them with a fabric the customer supplies. The canvas shades are treated against fire, water, dirt, and mildew, and, handcrated by Castec, are as attractive as many much higher-priced Roman shades.

The range of colors for this series includes dusty rose, taupe, and teal. The matte-finished, rotary-screen-printed wallpaper comes in sixty-five different styles, and coordinated fabrics and borders are available.

For further information, contact:

Sterling Prints
23645 Mercantile Rd.
Cleveland, OH 44122
(216) 464-3700

STERLING PRINTS

The desert prints of Helen Webber are a far cry from dainty English floral prints. Liberal ribbons of colors streak across the wallcoverings. Waves and the fabric Ripples, two designs from the Tapestry Collection of wallcoverings shown here, suggest the mesas and flowing clouds of the Southwest.

For more information, contact:

Castec Inc.
7531 Coldwater Canyon Ave.
North Hollywood, CA 91605
(818) 503-8300

KIRSCH

The slenderness of 1″-thick Kirsch mini-blinds render them practically invisible when tilted open, and an elegant addition to a room's design when closed. The blinds come cut to the customer's requested measure.

For more information about mini-blinds, as well as Kirsch's wood blinds and vertical blinds, contact:

Kirsch Co.
309 N. Prospect St.
P.O. Box 0370
Sturgis, MI 49091
(616) 651-0211

NANIK

The increasing popularity of unusual shapes for windows has challenged

makers of window-blinds to adapt their products. Nanik, a maker of hardwood blinds, has met this challenge and is now able to satisfy almost any demand a customer might make. Nanik can adapt its blinds to fit arches, such as the one shown here, or A-frame, tapered, circular, or even octagonal windows. Nanik can custom-make blinds to fit further demands, such as providing spaces in them for air-conditioners, or combining different styles of blinds for a desired effect. Nanik makes a large range of hardwood blinds, both horizontal and vertical, as well as some resin-based blinds.

For more information, contact:

Nanik
7200 Stewart Ave.
Wausau, WI 54401
(715) 842-4653

VEROSOL

For those who do not like Venetian blinds, pleated shades from Verosol are an attractive alternative. In a humid and hot region such as Florida, the shades perform several useful functions. They shut out a high amount of heat in the summer and do not become mildewed because of their aluminum fabric composition. Verosol makes several different shades and can adapt them to unusual architectural shapes.

For more information, contact:

Verosol, USA, Inc.
224 Park West Drive
RIDC Park West
Pittsburgh, PA 15275
(412) 787-9810

Other Suppliers of Decorative Finishes

Consult List of Suppliers for addresses.

Textiles

Auger Designs Ltd.
Charles Barone Inc.
Joel Berman Associates, Inc.
Conran's
Donghia Associates, Inc.
Fabricut Fabrics
Fabri-Trak, Unique Concepts Inc.
Finlandia Fabrics
General Drapery Services, Inc.
S. M. Hexter Co.
Imperial Wallcoverings
Jensen-Lewis Co. Inc.
Katzenbach and Warren, Inc.
Lisa Lamb
The October Co., Inc.
OJVM Linen Wallcoverings
Maya Romanoff Textiles
Rosecore Handprints
Scalamandré Inc.
Sterling Prints
V'soski Shops, Inc.
Westgate Fabrics, Inc.

Ceramics

Amaru Tile International
Designers Tile International
Elon, Inc.
Forms and Surfaces
Hastings Tile and Il Bagno
Marazzi USA, Inc.
Marble Concepts
Puccio/European Marble Works Inc.
Villeroy & Boch (USA) Inc.
Walker & Zanger
Waterworks

Floor Coverings

Armstrong World Industries, Inc.
Celia, Inc.
Colonnade Carpets, Collins & Aikman Corp.
A. T. Euster Furniture Co.
Furniture of the Twentieth Century, Inc.
Floordesigns, Inc.
Gulistan Carpet by J. P. Stevens & Co. Inc.
Harmony Carpet Corp.
Karastan Rug Mills
Kenmore Carpet Corp.
Lees Carpet
Milliken and Company
Mohawk Carpet
Patterson, Flynn & Martin Inc.
Saxony Carpet Co., Inc.

Laminates

Chemetal Corp.
Copperlite Corp.
E. I. Du Pont de Nemours & Co., Inc.
Formica Corp.

Papers

Carefree Wallcoverings
China Seas, Inc.
United Wallcoverings

Shades and Blinds

Joel Berman Associates, Inc.
Norman Blumenthal
Hunter Douglas Inc.
I.D. International
Levolor Lorentzen, Inc.
Mecho Shade Corp.
Mohawk Industries, Inc.
Wesco Fabrics Inc.

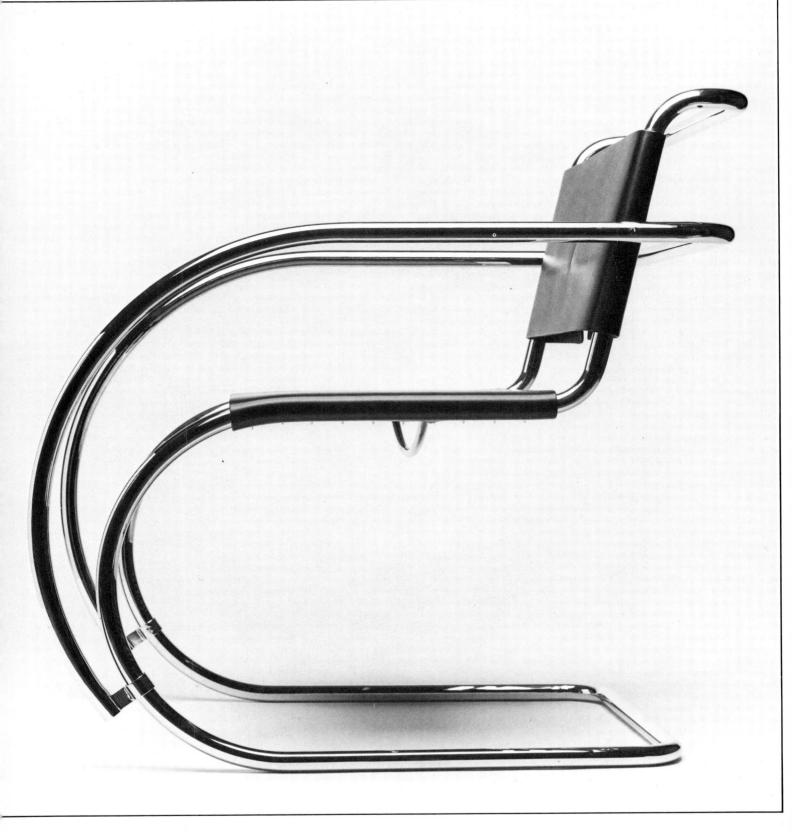

5.
Furniture

The furnishings of a modern house have long been of great interest to imaginative designers and craftsmen. Architects such as Mies van der Rohe and Frank Lloyd Wright were as interested in furniture design as in architectural plans. Today, other leading architects such as Robert Venturi and Michael Graves and thousands of other skilled artisans are engaged in the production of useful and pleasing furniture for all areas of the home.

The opportunities to acquire quality contemporary furniture are many. Costs range widely from one-of-a-kind craftsman-designed-and-built masterpieces to mass-produced factory pieces. Some of the best modern furniture is simple in construction and modest in price. European retailers such as Conran and IKEA, and American counterparts like Workbench and The Door Store, have expanded the availability of well-designed, affordable furnishings.

Many of the pieces illustrated in the following pages are available directly from the manufacturer or craftsman or from selected retail outlets, the names of which will be supplied upon request by the maker. Included are many types of sofas, chairs, tables, beds, rockers, and storage units. Some are classics of modern style such as the Mies van der Rohe MR chair illustrated opposite; others produced by today's craftsmen are on their way to becoming contemporary classics. All share an originality of design and a quality of craftsmanship which recommend them for long-term use. And each piece of furniture—whether first produced in the 1920s or the '80s—possesses a contemporary character fully in keeping with a modern architectural setting.

MR armchair by Mies van der Rohe, 1927, in wicker as manufactured by Palazzetti, Inc.

Sofas, Settees, Love Seats, and Benches

Furniture for seating two or more people falls roughly into two categories—standard, mass-produced pieces or handcrafted ones. Plush, fully upholstered sofas, the mainstay of American living rooms for decades, continue to be immensely popular. Variations on the standard shape of this piece of furniture are not often dramatic, though—usually a slant or a roll to the armrest is all you will find. Presented here, however, are a selection of mass-produced contemporary sofas that incorporate handsome innovations, such as sharply angled backs and sides, flowering shapes, and so on. Even more daring are modern craftsmen who are creating contemporary furniture with imaginatively sculpted legs and backs. These furniture makers usually upholster their sofas sparingly, so as not to blur the striking designs. Furniture as diverse as a well-stuffed sofa from Thayer-Coggin and a lightning bolt bench from Jon Brooks share a common quality, namely durability. Their tough construction will withstand heavy use for years to come.

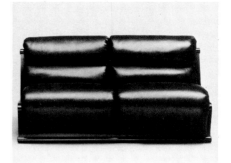

JAZZ TWO-SEATER

The seat of the Jazz Two-Seater from Dakota Jackson rises up to support the body in a truly relaxing position. Plush leather upholstery rests on a lacquered bentwood frame with anodized metal dowels running along its length. The Two-Seater measures 60″ long, 36″ deep, and 30″ high. Single-seat and three-seat versions are also available in this design.

For further information, contact:

Dakota Jackson Inc.
306 E. 61st St.
New York, NY 10021
(212) 838-9444

CONTATTO SETTEE

The layers of cushions on the Contatto high-back settee create an energetic design, and yet they also make the settee very comfortable. Made in Italy by Brunati, it is available through Axiom Designs. Molded polyurethane cushions can be upholstered with a selection from Brunati's collection of fabrics.

For more information, contact:

Axiom Designs
110 Greene St.
New York, NY 10012
(212) 219-2212

RIBBONBACK LOVE SEAT

Historically, ribbonbacks have been so flowery and ornate that their splats resemble snarls more than ribbons. Designers John Wall and Michael Goldfinger have stripped the style to its basic constituent—a long, slender, curving ribbon of wood serving as a back. The love seat shown here is part of a series of ribbonback pieces made of Honduras mahogany and finished in either natural or black lacquer. Measuring 47″ wide, 24″ deep, and 30″ high, the love seat is also available with an upholstered seat and back.

For further information, contact:

Wall • Goldfinger Design Associates
7 Belknap St.
Northfield, VT 05663
(802) 485-6261

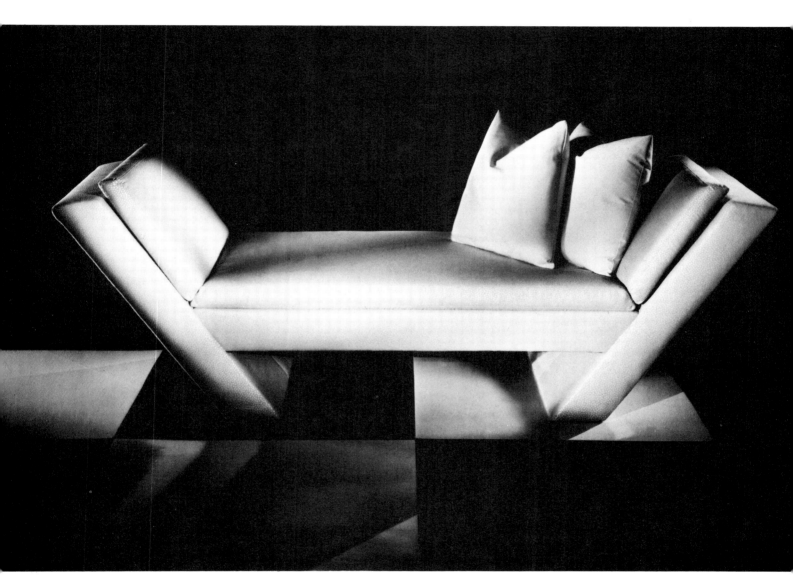

2646 CHAISE

Thayer Coggin's cantilevered chaise is one of the most unusual custom pieces produced by this major furniture manufacturer. 90″ wide at the broadest point, it provides more than adequate space for reclining. It is engineered to support even a plump person. Completely upholstered, the space-age chaise is supplied with two side pieces and a seating pad. The chaise is 31″ deep and stands 31″ high.

Catalogue, $4.

Thayer Coggin Inc.
427 South Rd.
P.O. Box 5867
High Point, NC 27262
(919) 889-1700

PULLMAN SOFA

Both the Pullman sofa and armchair feature a back that wraps around the piece to form the arms. The back cushions, cradled as they are, resemble throw pillows more than blocks of foam. These gently rounded pieces feature comfortable back and seat cushions and are upholstered in suede, as shown here, or in a variety of other materials.

For further information, contact:

Karl Springer Ltd.
306 E. 61st St.
New York, NY 10021
(212) 752-1695

ASTER

Aster couches and armchairs are made by Busnelli of Italy and are available through the Greenbaum Collection. Upholstered in glove leather, the Aster comes in two- and three-seat sofas (measuring 60″ or 83″ long, 37″ high, and 32″ deep) or armchairs (measuring 38″ long, 37″ high, and 32″ deep).

For more information about these and

other imported models from the collection, contact:

Greenbaum Collection
101 Washington St.
Paterson, NJ 07505
(201) 279-3000

MONIQUE SOFA

Every part of the Monique sofa serves to comfort the seated individual. Fully upholstered in leather, fabric, or suede, it has a wraparound back and low pillow-like armrests. Designed by S. Parravicini for Mariani, it comes with matching or contrasting welting and stitching. The Pace Collection also offers Monique as a two-seat sofa, armchair, and ottoman.

For further information, contact:

The Pace Collection, Inc.
11-11 34th Ave.
Long Island City, NY 11106
(718) 721-8201

LA LUNE WILLOW SOFA

Willow-branch furniture may resemble wicker, but with their heavy bark and thick limbs, willow pieces are more energetic and arresting. The sofa by La Lune shown here displays slender curving branches and solid long limbs in its construction. The sofa measures 72″ in length, 40″ in height, and 34″ in depth, and is also available in a smaller size or as a love seat.

For further information, contact:

La Lune Willow Collection
241 N. Broadway
Milwaukee, WI 53202
(414) 271-1172

ADAGIO SOFA

Designed by Dennis L. Christiansen, the Adagio sofa has rolled edges that are somewhat exaggerated to give the piece a strong, flaring appearance as well as comfortable armrests. Shown here with a matching chair, the sofa measures 100″ long and is 25″ high and 35″ deep. The single slab seat cushion is inner-lined with an extra cover which is sewn into a loose outer surface. The Adagio group also includes a shorter 75″ sofa.

For further information, contact:

Dunbar
601 S. Fulton St.
Berne, IN 46711
(219) 589-2111

SPACE

Designed by Nicola Trussardi for Scalia, Space is a truly innovative contemporary sofa. The cushion units, made of variable-density polyurethane and acrylic fibers with glossy leather upholstery, are pre-formed. A row of plexiglass blades support the cushions, and the assembly rests on a frame of gun-barrel metal pipe with a

bronze or brushed nickel finish. Shown here is the two-seat model, which measures 57" wide, 35" deep, and 31" high. Space also comes as a three-seat sofa or lounge chair. A plexiglass arm is also available which can be easily joined to the frame, extending the sofa's length 4".

For further information, contact:

Greenbaum Collection
101 Washington St.
Paterson, NJ 07505
(201) 279-3000

SLANT SOFA

Thayer Coggin has a knack for making modular sofas more than merely islands of blocks. The angles of the slanting sofa shown here give it an architectural aspect that vitalizes it, turning the piece into a major element of any room's design. The back rises from 24" at either end to 37¼". The main sofa module measures 35" deep, 84" long, and the sectional unit measures 35" deep and 81" long. Also shown is a 66" by 35" by 37½" coordinated chaise and a matching table.

Catalogue, $4.

Thayer Coggin Inc.
427 South Rd.
P.O. Box 5867
High Point, NC 27262
(919) 889-1700

HARDWICK SOFA

The warm design of the Hardwick sofa, from Peter Miles Furniture of England and imported by Interna Designs, makes it a sophisticated yet comfortable addition to the living room. The full, curved structure of the sofa serves to highlight the hand-woven Scottish tapestries draped across the seat and over the back. Both the tapestry and the upholstery are made of wool, although the sofa can also be covered with leather or other fabrics. The Hardwick measures 26½" high, 40½" deep, and 82" long.

For further information, contact:

Interna Designs, Ltd.
The Merchandise Mart
Space 6-168
Chicago, IL 60654
(312) 467-6076

CLUB SOFA SERIES

Donghia Furniture, founded by Angelo Donghia, offers several variations on the traditional couch in its Club Sofa series. All of them are 72″ long and incorporate a vigorous line of design. Shown here are the Main Street and Madison models. The open-base Main Street has high solid armrests and contrasting welting that give it a sensation of fullness. The full, yet sleek, Madison features rolled arms and front legs upholstered in Mohair Stripe, a Donghia textile combining wool and mohair with dyed stripes.

For more information, contact:

Donghia Furniture
485 Broadway
New York, NY 10013
(212) 925-2777

2110 SOFA

Thayer Coggin's 88"-long sofa features rolled edges with tucked folds. The bun feet shown here are optional; normally the sofa comes with recessed block legs. Measuring 42½" deep and 34½" high, it is available in a range of colors and fabrics.

Catalogue, $4.

Thayer Coggin Inc.
427 South Rd.
P.O. Box 5867
High Point, NC 27262
(919) 889-1700

AURA

The Aura two-seat sofa retains the compactness and unity of design of a chair. Designed by Paola Piva for the deSede of Switzerland collection, the design is also available in a lounge chair or a three-seat sofa, each with beech wood feet. The lines of the flowing Aura design can be accentuated by using welting which con-

trasts with the upholstery fabric. Stendig offers this furniture in a range of leathers and fabrics.

For further information, contact:

Stendig, Inc.
410 E. 62nd St.
New York, NY 10021
(212) 838-6050

HAGUE SOFA

Gerard van den Berg joins the lightness of a wicker-like frame with the comfort of a well-cushioned couch in his Hague sofa. Woven saleen, a newly developed European synthetic fiber, is fused with a slender metal frame in chrome or charcoal coloring. The seat, back, and arms form an in-viting bucket shape, upholstered in leather or fabric.

For further information, contact:

Casa Bella Imports
215 E. 58th St.
New York, NY 10022
(212) 688-2020

Geoffrey Katz

PIANO BENCH

The contemplative tone of the sculptural elements of Jon Brooks's piano bench give it a more spiritual affinity to the piano than a physical one. Made of walnut, sugar pine, and cherry, it stands 24″ high and measures 24″ wide and 48″ long.

For further information, contact:

Jon Brooks
Pine Rd.
New Boston, NH 03070
(603) 487-2780

GULL SOFA

Instead of jutting up like walls, the arms of the Gull sofa slant into the seat. Consequently, not only do they cradle a person seated at either end, but they make the Gull perfect for leisurely sprawling. Designed by Burkhard Vogtherr, the Gull comes in any of Brayton's large selection of fabrics and leathers. It measures 78¾″ wide, 33″ deep, and 29½″ high. Gull is also available as a chair or as a two-seat sofa.

For further information, contact:

Brayton International Collection
255 Swathmore Ave.
P.O. Box 7288
High Point, NC 27264
(919) 434-4151

Geoffrey Katz

QUATRAIN TASMANIA

Jon Brooks's works are continually pushing the limits of furniture into the realm of sculpture. Quatrain Tasmania, shown here, is one such example. The three elements—an almost liquid slab and two sharply cut supports of Tasmanian blackwood, with a bolt of Huon pine—create jarring contrasts. The bench measures 20″ high, 20″ wide, and 72″ long.

For more information, contact:

Jon Brooks
Pine Rd.
New Boston, NH 03070
(603) 487-2780

Glenn Moody

POST BENCH

John Wall and Michael Goldfinger expose the skillfully carved and detailed wood of their furniture for a stately effect. The post bench has the proper angles of a Puritan pew, and yet the scored detailing and deep, solid mahogany construction give it a contemporary elegance. The bench comes in a natural, dark, or black mahogany finish with lacquer. Custom woods can also be specially ordered. The back is 32″ high and the seat is 22″ deep; the bench is available in lengths ranging from 48″ to 84″. Upholstery can be ordered for the back and seat.

For further information, contact:

**Wall • Goldfinger Design Associates
7 Belknap St.
Northfield, VT 05663
(802) 485-6261**

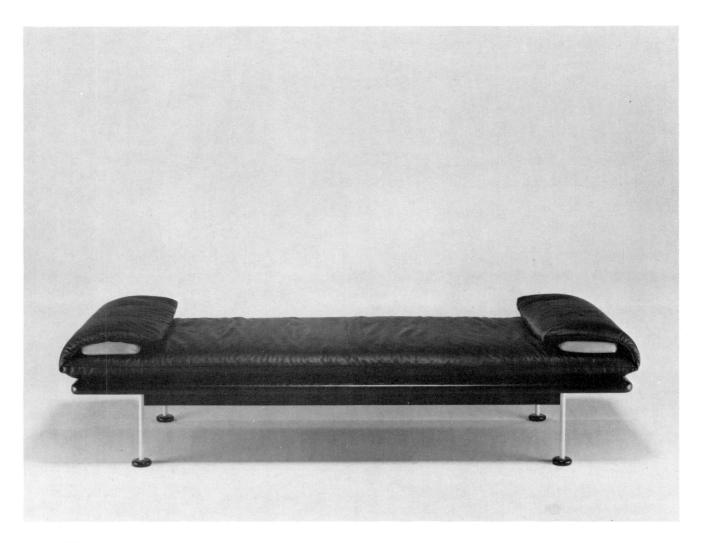

GRAFFITI

Designed by Burkhard Vogtherr, the Graffiti displays the spareness of design found in any well-made International-style piece of furniture, as well as its luxury. It consists of a slab cushion with low bolsters at each end, and thin ash legs. The bench measures 81″ by 28½″ by 18¾″. The seat is available in a wide range of fabrics and leathers, while the bolsters and legs come in red, black, or gray. The frame can be finished in gray, ebony, or a natural tone.

For further information, contact:

Brayton International Collection
255 Swathmore Ave.
P.O. Box 7288
High Point, NC 27264
(919) 434-4151

LIVERPOOL

Designer Ronald Carter elongates the back of the classic garden bench to give Liverpool its elegantly contemporary proportions. Made by Peter Miles Furniture of England and imported by Interna Designs, Liverpool comes with optional canvas and foam cushions fitted to the slightly curved seat. Available with a natural finish, it measures 43¼″ high overall, 59¼″ wide, and 23½″ deep.

For further information, contact:

Interna Designs, Ltd.
The Merchandise Mart
Space 6-168
Chicago, IL 60654
(312) 467-6076

WRIGHT COUCH

Accurate reproductions of furniture from modern masters of design are more than just oddities like miniature Rolls Royces. Because the care and skill the designer demanded are often preserved among the better replicas, these pieces are excellent, durable furniture. Heinz & Co. reproduces such classic Frank Lloyd Wright pieces as the spindle couch shown here. Designed for the Greene House in Aurora, Illinois, this 6' 4" couch boasts Wright's masterful yet simple proportions of construction. Heinz & Co. does not scrimp on precision, and so objects such as this couch (which requires oak veneers and 90° laminations) take unusual amounts of effort to build.

For further information, contact:

Heinz & Co.
P.O. Box 663
Oak Park, IL 60303
(312) 383-1310

Tables

Tables can be the most imaginative and sculptural of all types of furniture, since the only requirement is a flat horizontal surface. Consequently, table designs cover an enormous spectrum of modern styles. Some designs recall the turn of the century and the craftsmen of the Arts and Crafts movement who made sturdy and sensible wooden furniture. Other models are reminiscent of the design revolution of the '20s, such as modern reproductions of Wright and LeCorbusier tables. The consumer can choose between the luxurious gleaming Art Deco pieces or the practical modular plastic models when looking for tables. The most recent addition to these styles has been the eccentric but fascinating work of individual craftsmen. Given the unusual forms worked by these postmodern masters, it's difficult to imagine what new shapes the exhaustively modified table will take in the future.

Cocktail/Coffee Tables

SPIDER TABLE

The simplicity of Peter Danko's Spider table doesn't seem contrived or strained—he makes it seem as if tables have always been meant to have this unusually sculpted design.

Three flowing molded legs of cherry, ash, or walnut meet at an inlaid triangle of ebony or white maple. The 18"-high stand supports a 25"-wide glass top.

For further information, contact:

Peter Danko & Associates, Inc.
7492-F Old Alexander Ferry Rd.
Clinton, MD 20735
(301) 292-1653

top. The table measures 48" by 36" by 16".

For further information, contact:

SQUARE COCKTAIL TABLE

The Gio Collection from Casa Stradivari consists of occasional tables, game tables, and the cocktail table shown here. The geometrical inlaid pattern, here made of dyed bird's-eye maple, characterizes all of the Gio furniture. The table tops are available in color combinations of red, gray, lavender, blue, and white, as well as in a natural tint. This table is finished with high gloss polyurethane and

Dakota Jackson, Inc.
306 E. 61st St.
New York, NY 10021
(212) 838-9444

measures 40" square and stands 15½" high.

For more information, contact:

Casa Stradivari
221 McKibbin St.
Brooklyn, NY 11206
(718) 386-0048

JAZZ COCKTAIL TABLE

Two elegant lacquered pedestals form the base of the Jazz cocktail table from Dakota Jackson. Made of contrasting anodized and unanodized metal, they have scored detailing which contrasts nicely with the smooth plane of the ⅝"-thick glass

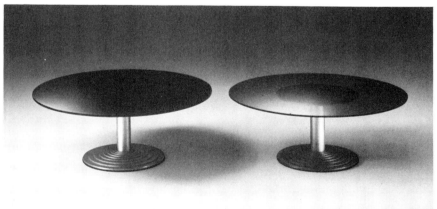

THE FUSIONS

The low, graceful proportions of The Fusions tables from Origlia remind one of some sort of exotic raintree.

The base of each stands only 14¾" high, and the table top is 30½" in diameter, serving well for a coffee table. The ridge pedestal adds to the pleasing design, as well as the combination of either burgundy-colored wood or bronzed crystal with a chrome- or brass-plated base.

For more information, contact:

Origlia USA Inc.
200 Lexington Ave.
New York, NY 10016
(212) 532-0075

GINGER LEAF TABLE

At one end of the spectrum of furniture design are those craftsmen who believe that beauty is efficiency, that tables are machines, and that all things ought to serve practical purposes. Mark Levin is not one of these people. He is probably aware that Le Corbusier would not have been pleased with a Ginger Leaf table, but Levin is probably not trying to please him anyway. Each of his works is tightly unified around one decorative

theme. For this one, he has chosen a waving motif, and has carved frills from laminated Honduras mahogany. With three legs and dimensions of 28″ by 60″ by 32″, Levin's table can serve as a remarkable desk as well.

For further information, contact:

Mark S. Levin
914 Thomas St.
Oak Park, IL 60302
(312) 848-5343

REDWOOD TABLE

Although some of sculptor J.B. Blunk's works are furniture, they always reflect his overpowering concern with the combination of art and nature. The coffee table shown here provides a relatively smooth and regular top surface with a bowl insert, but underneath the redwood swirls in patterns of its own liking. The table was designed in 1981 and measures 44″ by 18″ by 23″. Blunk's other

Thomas Weir

"utilitarian sculptures" include chairs and larger tables.

Catalogue available.

J.B. Blunk
P.O. Box 83
Inverness, CA 94937
(415) 669-1458

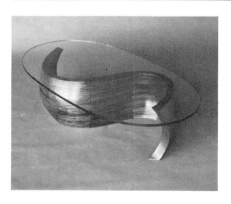

S CURVE COFFEE TABLE

George Berry's S-shaped coffee table is an example of his enormous care in the construction of furniture. The walnut base, handmade and hand-finished, requires about three months of Berry's labor to make. Including the glass top, the table measures 36″ wide, 60″ long, and 16½″ high.

For more information, contact:

George Berry
745 Edgewood Ave. N.E.
Atlanta, GA 30307
(404) 577-4433

PHILIPPE COFFEE TABLE

Acrylic, brass, and glass make a stunning Art Deco combination in the Philippe coffee table by Plexability.

Paul Aresu

Black acrylic pedestals, shaped like Century of Progress pylons, curve over the inserted table top. The rounded brass apron provides a contrasting, more subtle gleam, and the glass surface is decorated with a single, elegant matte stripe. The table measures 37″ square and 17″ high.

For more information, contact:

Plexability
New York Design Building
Suite 506
200 Lexington Ave.
New York, NY 10016
(212) 679-7826

EMERALD COFFEE TABLE

The prismatic facets of this coffee table, resembling those of cut gems,

Paul Aresu

reflect and refract light at a myriad of angles. The acrylic legs and apron are cut 3″ thick and hold a glass table top. The Emerald table shown here measures 28″ wide, 22″ long, and 16½″ high; it comes in other custom sizes as well.

For more information, contact:

Plexability
New York Design Building
Suite 506
200 Lexington Ave.
New York, NY 10016
(212) 679-7826

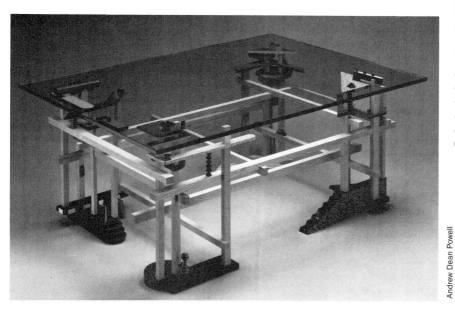

Andrew Dean Powell

MONOPOLY TABLE

Underneath the Monopoly table's practical 42″ by 36″ plate of glass is a labyrinth of eccentric and high-spirited woodwork and detailing. Parts of the 18″-high pedestal are enameled and the rest has a natural wood finish. Tom Loeser, the table's extraordinary designer, constructs unique pieces of furniture on commission or for galleries. He has displayed his work in

many shows and has pieces in the Cooper-Hewitt Museum collection in New York City.

For further information, contact:

Tom Loeser
16 Emily St.
Cambridge, MA 02139
(617) 661-9836

MODERN AGE TABLE

Modern Age Galleries, which David and Christine Van der Hurd manage, offers Italian, English, and American works in modern design as well as Christine Van der Hurd's own postmodern designs. Among the collection are examples of Art Deco furniture, tubular chrome furniture from the '30s, and works by Italian architect Carlo Scarpa.

Christine Van der Hurd designs vases, mirrors, and tables with an unquestionably personal style, featuring explosive collages of shapes such as those on the coffee table shown here.

A flurry of triangles and rectangles are etched on a glass table top which is supported by curving legs.

For further information, contact:

Modern Age Galleries
795 Broadway
New York, NY 10003
(212) 674-5603

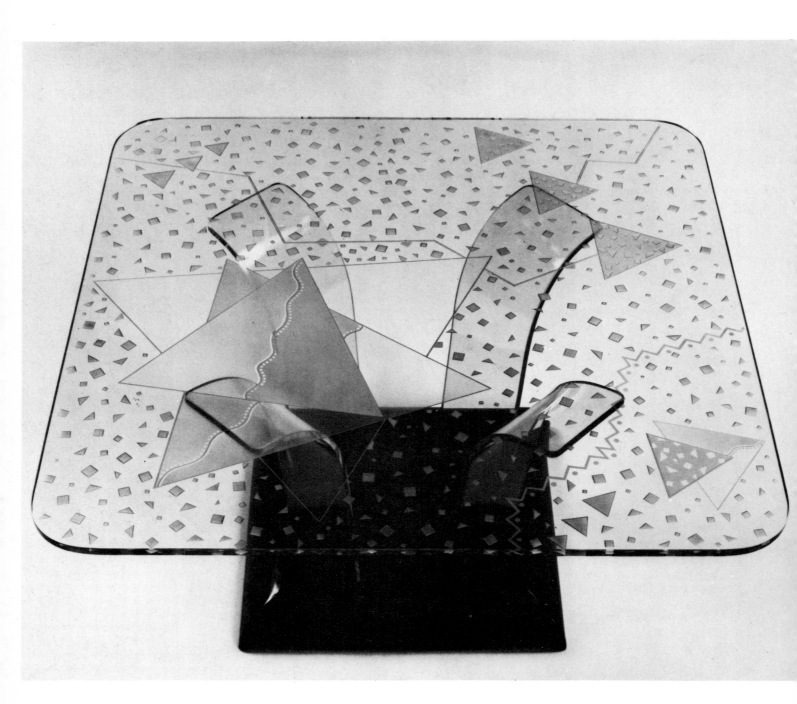

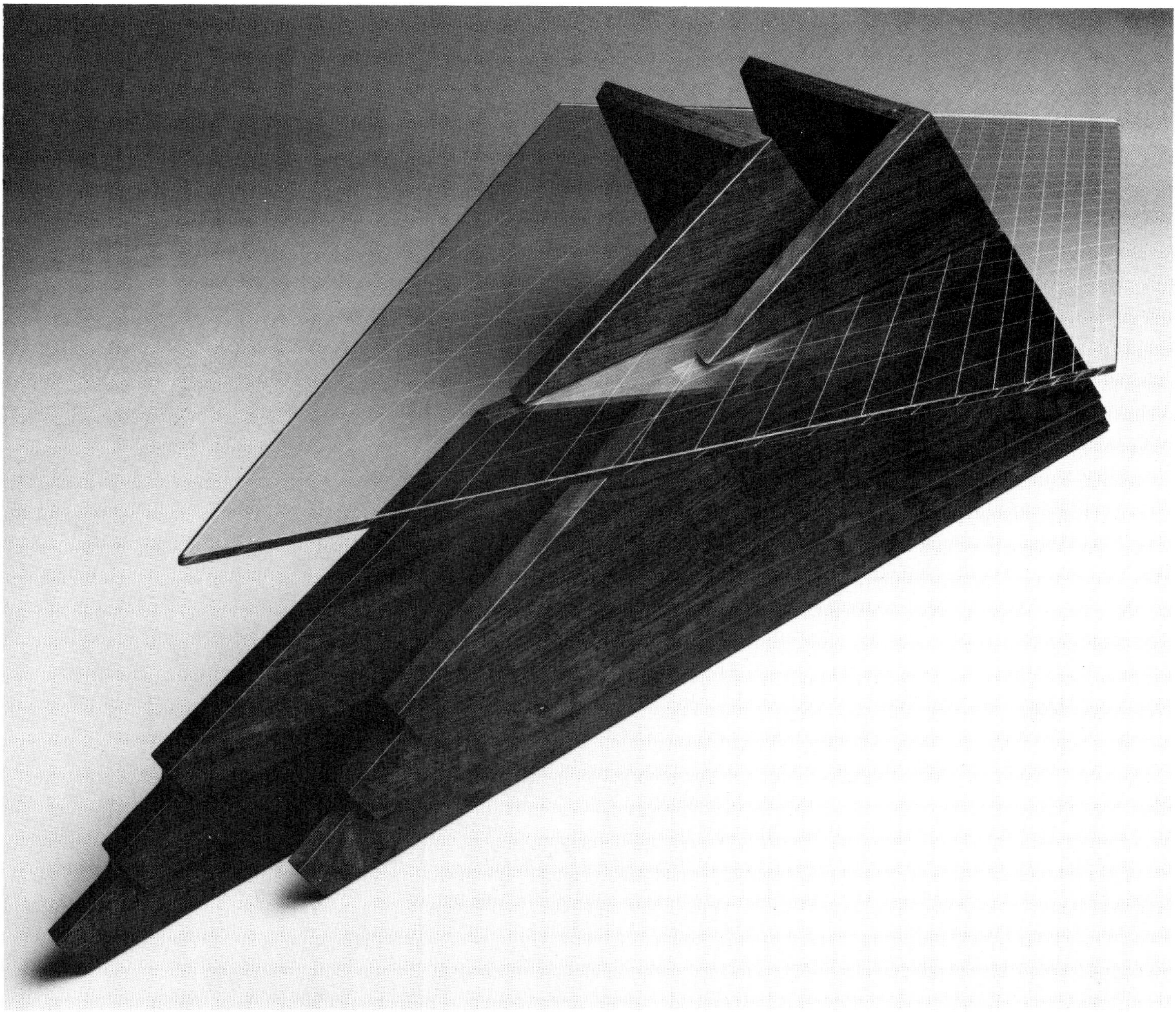

COFFEE TABLE

Robert Chehayl's impressive coffee table consists of a trapezium of glass with an unusual grid pattern and two triangular pedestals made of purpleheart, a South American wood. Measuring 20″ high, 46″ wide, and 93″ long, it combines glass and wood so sculpturally that its use as a coffee table seems almost like a happy after-thought. Robert Chehayl designs and makes one-of-a-kind pieces of wooden furniture, each more than likely to become a treasured heirloom in the future.

For further information about Robert Chehayl's work, contact:

**Robert Chehayl
49 Harrison St.
Hoboken, NJ 07030
(201) 798-3018**

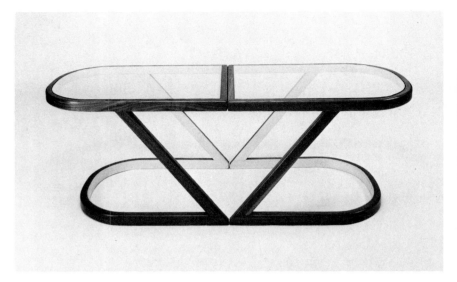

Z TABLES

René Soulard's Z tables have the same strength of composition as the works of Gerrit Rietveld and De Stijl. Together, they can serve as a coffee table; separated, they are excellent end or cocktail tables. They stand 18" high and are 22" wide and 36" long. Soulard uses this design for his dining room tables, coffee tables, and chairs as well.

For further information, contact:

René Soulard
1833 13th Ave. #208
Seattle, WA 98122
(206) 328-1164

MARK II TABLE

Leather tables are certainly uncommon, and Karl Springer's Mark II table, covered in leather, is made truly unusual by the additional use of bronze inlaid detail and bronze-tinted glass. The Mark II comes in custom sizes and finishes; it is available through architects, specifiers, and designers.

For further information, contact:

Karl Springer, Ltd.
306 E. 61st St.
New York, NY 10021
(212) 752-1695

VENTURI LOW TABLES

Part of Robert Venturi's collection of furniture for Knoll, these low tables complement his group of postmodern pieces, although their subdued design and colors make them appropriate for other contemporary settings as well. The base is made of fiberglass; the glass top is either clear or black. An applied acrylic enamel pattern or a monochromatic finish are available. The table top measures 44" in diameter and comes with a 2½" maple edge. The tables measure 14" high.

For further information, contact:

Knoll International
The Knoll Building
655 Madison Ave.
New York, NY 10021
(212) 826-2400

JOHN MARCOUX TABLES

John Marcoux builds furniture on commission, such as the tables shown here. Much of his work has recently been concerned with turning structural elements of furniture into ornamental ones as well.

The web-like joints of his Pentacle table require no glue. Instead, bolt connections are plainly displayed, not only lending to the table's durability,

but also to its functional attractiveness. The criss-crossing supports form numerous geometric shapes, such as pentagons, five-pointed stars, and tetrahedrons. The table is just about as sturdy as physically possible. Measuring 18″ high and 34″ wide, it is made of varnished maple with a ⅜″-thick plate-glass top.

Looking at the seemingly chaotic base of the Trinal table through the glass top is something like looking through the wall of an aquarium at a flurry of colorful sea creatures. The red, green, and yellow painted wooden legs create a busy network of lines, supported by steel connectors and bolts. The table measures 18″ high and the ⅜″-thick glass top is 32″ across.

EDGE 54

A coffee table generally does not deserve the trappings of luxury, but designers John Wall and Michael Goldfinger have lavished it on their Edge 54 table nonetheless. The pedestal, four rectangular pillars 16″ high, and the edging on the table top are made of Honduras mahogany with natural lacquer. The table top itself is an expansive, 42″-square sheet of polished black onyx, as is the base. All in all, it is nothing short of wonderful.

For further information, contact:

Wall • Goldfinger Design Associates
7 Belknap St.
Northfield, VT 05663
(802) 485-6261

Bert Beaver

For further information, contact:

John Marcoux
283 George St.
Providence, RI 02906
(401) 351-1398

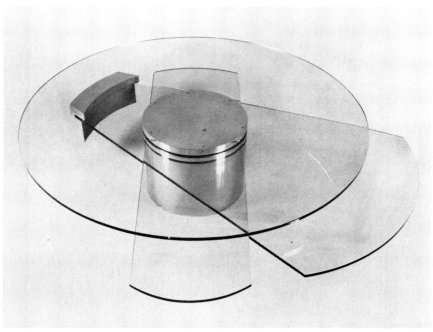

REVOLVING COFFEE TABLE

The revolving glass wings on Dakota Jackson's coffee table are as practical for passing drinks around as they are attractive. One wing is a regular rectangle, while the other is a fan-shaped piece with a brass counterweight at one end. The ¾″-thick top level of glass does not rotate. With a brass pedestal that echoes the material of the counterweight, the entire table measures 58″ wide and 17″ high.

For further information, contact:

Dakota Jackson Inc.
306 E. 61st St.
New York, NY 10021
(212) 838-9444

CAROUSEL DINING TABLE

Pritam & Eames offers a powerfully coordinated dining table set designed by David Powell. The table and chairs are tipped with ebony, which in both color and texture contrasts deeply with the set's maple construction. In addition, the dining table has ebony edging and a black granite lazy Susan on a ball bearing carriage. The table top is made of alternating sections of figure crotch and flatsewn maple. The

chairs, measuring 22½" wide, 33½" high, and 22½" deep, have black silk upholstery which matches the ebony detailing. The table measures 60" wide and 29" high.

For further information, contact:

Pritam & Eames
29 Race Lane
East Hampton, NY 11937
(516) 324-7111

TRI-TABLE

The slightly modified features of Michael Chinn's extraordinary Tri-

Table—diamond shaped legs and a divided top—give it a subtle aura of

movement and power. Measuring 30" high, 48" wide, and 20" deep, it is made of purpleheart, hard maple, and Indian ebony, with scored detailing and an oil finish.

For further information about Chinn's unique design craftsmanship, contact:

Michael Chinn
Department of Art and Design
158 College of Design
Iowa State University
Ames, IA 50011
(515) 294-6724

Glenn Moody

QUADRANT CONFERENCE TABLE

John Wall and Michael Goldfinger specialize in designs that show to the best advantage the subtle elegance of wood. Shown here is a conference table from their Quadrant series, which includes desks, credenzas, and tables ranging in size from the one shown here down to end tables. The legs of the table, made of mahogany, have gentle cabriole-like curves. Contrasting with the frame is the broad table top, available in a veneer of curly maple, Macassar ebony, or other exotic woods.

For further information, contact:

Wall • Goldfinger Design Associates
7 Belknap St.
Northfield, VT 05663
(802) 485-6261

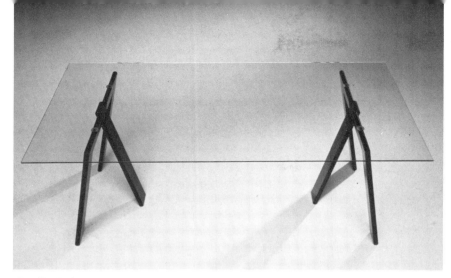

CHICHIBIO

The boldness of clear glass and brightly lacquered wood produces a strong design in this trestle table from Origlia. The trestle bases, designed sparely with three legs to each, come in white, gray, black, red, yellow, blue, or brown. The glass table top may be purchased in a variety of sizes.

For further information, contact:

Origlia USA Inc.
200 Lexington Ave.
New York, NY 10016
(212) 532-0075

duras mahogany supports. A thick, beveled cap of black onyx forms the table top. Antique marble is also available instead of onyx. The table comes with a natural, dark, or black mahogany stain with a lacquer finish. Special woods can be ordered for the table as well.

For further information, contact:

Wall • Goldfinger Design Associates
7 Belknap St.
Northfield, VT 05663
(802) 485-6261

TRILOGY

Shown here is one of the three Trilogy series tables designed by Norman Cherner and made by Modern Mode. The base descends from the table top as a column and then branches out into three feet, each with a wooden disk capped in stainless steel or bronze. Another Trilogy table has a similar base turned upside down, and the third has as its base three stylized Doric columns. All of the bases are made of chrome. The table tops

feature an S-shaped carved edge. They are available in oak, walnut, mahogany, cherry, or maple.

For further information, contact:

Modern Mode, Inc.
111 San Leandro Blvd.
San Leandro, CA 94577
(415) 568-6650

Glenn Moody

EDGE 54 DINING TABLE

The Edge 54 series of tables by Wall • Goldfinger, ranging from end tables to boardroom conference tables, displays magnificent proportions and craftsmanship. The dining table shown here stands on massive Hon-

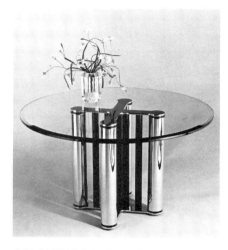

COLONNADE IV TABLE

Jeff Messerschmidt experiments boldly with combinations of stainless-steel columns in his Colonnade series of tables. Shown here is the Colonnade IV table, suitable as either a dining room or game table, with the arresting arrangement of a cross of columns. Plates cap the top and bottom of these columns, made of $\frac{1}{2}''$-thick stainless steel cut by laser with computer precision. $1\frac{5}{8}''$-diameter black acrylic rods follow the cross pattern between the columns. The $\frac{3}{4}''$-thick beveled-glass top measures 48″ in diameter, and the entire table is 28″ high.

For further information, contact:

Jeff Messerschmidt Designs
P.O. Box 382
Dallas, GA 30132
(404) 942-5949

134

ORA TABLE

David Estreich, an architect who frequently creates furniture for the houses he designs, preserves the beauty of Arts and Crafts designs of the turn of the century in his solidly constructed Ora table. Square, scored wooden legs support a granite top; the table also features spaced panels underneath. The table top is available in two sizes—84″ wide and 42″ deep or 72″ wide and 36″ deep—and the base is 29″ high.

For further information, contact:

Pace Collection, Inc.
11-11 34th Ave.
Long Island City, NY 11106
(718) 721-8201

NEW CLASSICS DINING TABLE

Postmodern designers, like their antecedents of the 1930s, are fond of rediscovering and then reinventing classicism. The scored detailing on Dakota Jackson's New Classics dining table, along with the combination of metal caps and a glass top, gives it a monumental Art Deco look, one that is more 1980s than 1930s. Made with bent cherry, the table measures 88″ long, 40″ wide, and 29″ high.

For further information, contact:

Dakota Jackson Inc.
306 E. 61st St.
New York, NY 10021
(212) 838-9444

LE CORBUSIER TABLE

First shown at the "Equipement intérieur d'une habitation" exhibit in Paris in 1929, Le Corbusier's table demonstrates some of the architect's concerns with timeless subjects of design such as shape and form. Approaching 60 years of age, the table has never really fallen out of style. The perfect proportions make it an excellent dining or conference table.

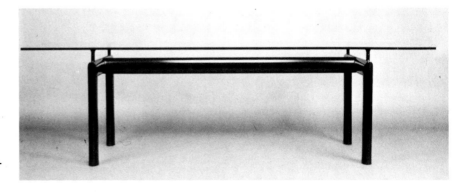

Oval steel tubes, finished with electrostatic epoxy, support either a glass or wood table top. The table measures 88½" by 33½" by 27½". Palazzetti, its manufacturer, creates replicas of many of Le Corbusier's works as well as those of other masters of modern design.

Catalogue, $15.

Palazzetti, Inc.
215 Lexington Ave.
New York, NY 10016
(212) 684-1199

DINING SET

The Thayer Coggin dining room set is tastefully coordinated with slender rectangular metal rods forming the table and chair bases. The ½"-thick glass table top, 42" by 78", is 29¼" high—sufficiently raised for easy clearance of the chairs. (The table shown here is model number 3502.) The chairs are available as armchairs (model number 1146) or side chairs (model number 1145). They measure 17½" wide, 27" deep, and 39" high.

Catalogue, $4.

Thayer Coggin Inc.
P.O. Box 5867
427 South Rd.
High Point, NC 27262
(919) 889-1700

THE VENTURI COLLECTION

Robert Venturi has made himself known through his architecture and writings as the father of postmodernism. He has branched out in his work to furniture, having designed a collection for Knoll. The Urn table and Cabriole table shown here are quintessentially postmodern, a revival of old motifs—not merely a form of Neo-Classicism, but more Neo-Everything. Styles from Art Deco to Renaissance Italian to Greek are exaggerated, superimposed on each other, and finally organized by a distinctly contemporary mind. The result is a whimsically perverse stateliness.

The Urn table has two pedestals that resemble 17th-century Tudor table bases, except that instead of being well-rounded blocks of wood, they are wood-laminations, resembling cardboard cutouts. The elongated table top, finished with wood veneer and edged with 1¼" of maple, adds to the pedestals' effect. The Urn table measures 120" long, 60" wide, and 28½" high.

The Cabriole table is an amusing choice for a postmodern experiment, since furniture-makers of the 1600s turned to the curving table leg after exhausting the variations on a straight leg, much as we may be exhausting modern rectilinearity today. The Cabriole is also made of wood lamina-

tions, with legs cut in rather deformed cabrioles and set at perpendicular angles. The pattern is typically postmodern as well—a bright pastel floral print with a superimposed scheme of short black lines, creating a vivaciously incongruous effect. The table measures 48″ square and 28½″ high.

For further information, contact:

Knoll International
The Knoll Building
655 Madison Ave.
New York, NY 10021
(212) 826-2400

HAARLEM II TRESTLE TABLE

Ronald Carter's classically-designed trestle table for the Peter Miles Collection is reminiscent of the best work of early 20th-century modern cabinetmakers. The clean, well-proportioned lines of the piece recommend it for home or office use. It is imported from England by Interna Designs. All of the furniture crafted at the Miles factory—much of which is designed by Carter—is constructed of solid English hardwoods such as oak, ash, and sycamore. The table illustrated is of oak, but other woods can be substituted. One cabinetmaker, rather than a group of assembly-line workers, assembles each piece. Changes can be made in the position of the solid-timber ladder-like trestles so as to allow for a different seating arrangement. The Haarlem II model shown here is 28″ in height, 96″ long, and 41″ wide; other sizes may be ordered.

For further information regarding this table and other Haarlem designs by Carter, contact:

Interna Designs, Ltd.
The Merchandise Mart
Space 6-168
Chicago, IL 60654
(312) 467-6076

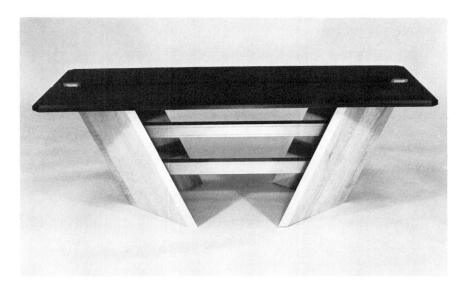

TENSION TABLE

Michael Chinn creates the feeling of a tug of war in his Tension table with sharply angled bases and horizontal braces. The table top is made of exotic wood while the support is hard maple. For the braces, Chinn uses Colorcore, a laminate with coloring distributed throughout rather than just on the surface. Measuring 18″ high, 49″ wide, and 21″ deep, the Tension

table can be used as a superbly original coffee table.

For further information, contact:

Michael Chinn
Department of Art and Design
158 College of Design
Iowa State University
Ames, IA 50011
(515) 294-6724

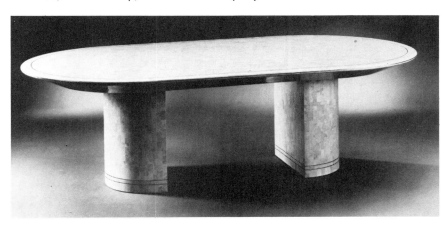

MARQUETRY CONFERENCE TABLE

Priests may have been performing sacrifices on tables like this a few thousand years ago, but now the massive proportions and broad table top are better suited to the ceremonial purposes of the conference center or the formal dining room. The Marquetry table's fossilized coral finish complements the decorative pedestal legs and inlaid brass. The oval table

top, with a knife edge, measures 96″. All in all, monumental but magnificent.

For further information, contact:

Karl Springer, Ltd.
306 E. 61st St.
New York, NY 10021
(212) 752-1695

End Tables

ART DECO PEDESTAL

The different levels of arcing acrylic in this Art Deco pedestal from Plexability create a sense of simultaneous spaciousness and massiveness. One pedestal can serve as the base for a chic cigarette table as shown here, or

Paul Aresu

several of the 16″-high fixtures can support a coffee table. Plexability offers an assortment of table tops in different sizes and colors.

For further information, contact:

Plexability
New York Design Building
Suite 506
200 Lexington Ave.
New York, NY 10016
(212) 679-7826

COMMA TABLE

No one ever said that a table must be only in the shape of a circle or a square, and Andy Pawlan has taken full advantage of that fact by designing the Comma. Fully resembling the punctuation mark of its name, this

table can wrap around corners at bedside or chairside. It comes in custom sizes and colors and is made of wood coated with a tough finish.

For more information, contact:

Cyrna International
Space 12-101
The Merchandise Mart
Chicago, IL 60654
(312) 329-0906

ORIGLIA END TABLES

Made of black Marquinia marble, Origlia's stately end table can accompany even the most contemporary of couches. These tables, from Origlia's Fusions collection, have bases — a rigid pedestal and a die-cast iron column—lacquered in black, and stand 28½″ high.

For further information, contact:

Origlia USA Inc.
200 Lexington Ave.
New York, NY 10016
(212) 532-0075

CONVERSIONS TABLE

Mickey and Roberta Ackerman, professors at the Rhode Island School of Design, create imaginative furniture, lighting fixtures, and jewelry at their workshop, Conversions. The Ackermans are very much gifted scavengers, as their end table shown here attests. Measuring 28″ by 12″ by 12″, it is made of materials—scraps of plastic and marble, tiny balls of brass— that one might find in a junkyard. The ingredients are arranged beautifully in a cement top and epoxy-coated steel frame.

For further information about unique Ackerman designs, contact:

Conversions
11 Sargent Ave.
Providence, RI 02906
(401) 831-7999

create imaginative pieces with details such as racing stripes or inlaid patterns.

For further information, contact:

General Mica Corp.
1850 N.E. 144th St.
N. Miami, FL 33181
(305) 949-7247

GEORGE BERRY TABLES

George Berry's painstaking craftsmanship results in beautiful furniture with impressive uses of wood. The coffee and end tables shown here, for example, are carved from single, unseamed pieces of French walnut. The edges have inlaid mahogany laminates along with dark-brown resin strips. The end tables measure 20" wide, 20" deep, and 22" high; the coffee table is 20" wide, 17" high, and 66" long.

For further information about these and other Berry designs, contact:

George Berry
745 Edgewood Ave., N.E.
Atlanta, GA 30307
(404) 577-4433

CURVATURE TABLES

The Curvature tables shown here serve as coffee tables, stacking tables, and even as a desk, but General Mica will make them in any dimensions the customer demands. In addition, General Mica has an enormous selection of laminates with which to make the tables and can

CORNER TABLE

Jeff Kellar's furniture has been featured in *American Craft*, the American Crafts Council's official magazine, and *The New York Times*. Each of the pieces he undertakes by commission is carefully assembled by hand, and the best materials are used. The handsome table illustrated here is especially handy for difficult-to-fill corners. It is constructed of East Indian rosewood with curly maple and stands 24" high and 17" on each side.

Kellar's showroom is open by appointment. To arrange a visit or to learn more about his work, contact:

Jeff Kellar, Furnituremaker
P.O. Box 4770
Portland, ME 04112
(207) 773-6269

DANCING TABLES

Used in hallways or next to chairs, Bob Trotman's Dancing Tables do not have to obey the laws of function that more frequently used furniture does. Under the playful hand of Trotman, they thus become sprightly objects that convey a feeling of whimsy as much as a purpose. The table is made of maple with polychromed lacquer, and the wooden legs seem to be in the process of shuffling across the floor. The Dancing Table has red and blue coloring on the top, along with natural wood and black highlights on the legs. The table stands 26″ high and the triangular top is 13″ to a side.

For further information, contact:

Bob Trotman
Rt. 1, Box 100-A2
Casar, NC 28020
(704) 538-8236

TERNARY TABLE

John Marcoux pushes the use of conventional hardware to a point at which it becomes simultaneously ornamental and structural. The marshalled hand-polished nuts and bolts at the base of the Ternary table, for example, are far more numerous than needed to keep the base together; they begin instead to resemble a row of gems. The base of the table, including the intersecting rods, is made of stainless steel. The table measures 29¼″ high, 16″ wide, and 15″ deep.

For further information, contact:

John Marcoux
283 George St.
Providence, RI 02906
(401) 351-1398

FLAMINGO TABLE

From his studio, Xylem, in Seattle, René Soulard creates furniture that generally revives the unmechanistic liveliness that has withered under the gaze of functionalists. His Flamingo table, for example, seems very much alive, as three 33"-tall pink birds support a 19" glass top. These creatures seem to be breeding, according to Soulard, since they are now taking the forms of coffee tables and entry tables, as well as a dining room set now in the planning stage.

For more information, contact:

René Soulard
1833 13th Ave., #208
Seattle, WA 98112
(206) 328-1164

THE PARENTHESIS NIGHT TABLE

Plexability uses both opaque and translucent acrylic for the Parenthesis night table, creating the illusion of a floating strip of color. The two clear acrylic legs stand 25" high. The colored console, available in a range of

Courtney Frisse

Paul Aresu

colors, measures 28" wide and 14½" long, and the drawer inside is 18" wide, 13" long, and 5⅞" deep.

For further information, contact:

Plexability
New York Design Building
Suite 506
200 Lexington Ave.
New York, NY 10016
(212) 679-7826

TRIANGULAR TABLES

Liza Lamb puts her handmade fabrics to a number of uses, such as attaching them to screen panels (described in chapter 1) and to paneled tables such as those shown here. The tops of the tables are glass, and the panels are 24" high and 18" wide. Lamb will often custom match her cotton Scotch-guarded fabrics with the interiors of the homes of her clients.

For further information, contact:

Liza Lamb Designs
533 Glenwood Rd.
Binghamton, NY 13905
(607) 770-0159

David Fishbein

CLASSIC CIGARETTE TABLE

The Classic Cigarette table by Michael Zevy Berkowicz of Plexability reinterprets the original International-style model by Eileen Gray. The acrylic pedestal houses a glass top, but the glass is treated so as to be indistinguishable from the rest of the table. Consequently, the reflected light and shadows from the table seem almost magical, forming the pattern of a leaf at the base of the pedestal. The model shown here measures 11½" wide and 18¼" high; the table may be ordered in other custom sizes as well.

For further information, contact:

144

Plexability
New York Design Building
Suite 506
200 Lexington Ave.
New York, NY 10016
(212) 679-7826

Side/Serving Tables

TRIO SIDE TABLE

The Trio side table, designed by Leon Rosen for the Pace Collection, consists of two circular tiers supported by

three black-lacquered spheres and three posts. The pleasingly simple table comes with a high-gloss veneer on the tiers and is 20″ high and 20″ in diameter. It is also available in other sizes and finishes.

For further information, contact:

The Pace Collection, Inc.
11-11 34th St.
Long Island City, NY 11106
(718) 721-8201

WRIGHT TABLE

Robert Heinz first made reproductions of Frank Lloyd Wright's furniture for owners of Wright-designed houses who were in need of appropriate furnishings. He has expanded his production with the firm of Heinz & Co. to the manufacture of twenty-four different furnishings, ranging from dinnerware to table lamps. Shown here is Wright's hexagonal side table, which

he designed for use in many of his houses. Its spare and compact geometry is typical of Wright's style.

For more information, contact:

Heinz & Co.
P.O. Box 663
Oak Park, IL 60303
(312) 383-1310

ARC SIDE TABLE

The contrasting panels of Dakota Jackson's Arc side table give it a distinctive postmodern appearance. The drawer is made of bird's-eye maple and the mildly curved sides are of cherry-stained mahogany. The table measures 26″ high, 26″ wide, and 18″ deep.

For further information, contact:

Dakota Jackson Inc.
306 E. 61st St.
New York, NY 10021
(212) 838-9444

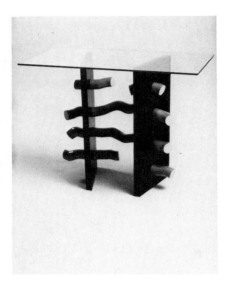

HALL TABLE

Writhing pieces of maple seem to swim between the vertical slabs of the exotic wood used in Tom Wessells' hall table. The table shown here is part of a series of furniture by Wessells, a Virginia woodworker who builds individual pieces on commission. A prime example of furniture as modern sculpture, the table measures 30″ by 36″ by 18″.

For further information about Wessells' work, contact:

Tom Wessells
4 Graham Dr.
Newport News, VA 23606
(804) 599-5615

NANCY, YOUR EARRINGS DON'T MATCH

Perhaps one of the few pieces of furniture on the market today with a chastisement as a title, this table has an equally unusual design by John Cannon. Piercing a regular black-lacquered Parsons table is a gold-leafed V (which leaves plenty of open space on the table top). Pendants (the ill-matched earrings, we assume)

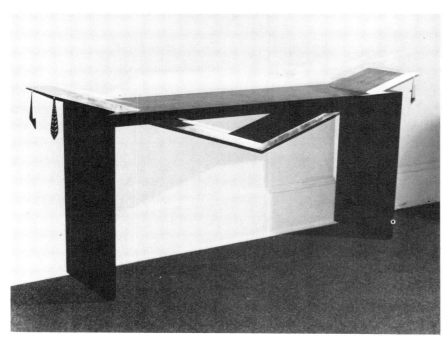

ing 39½″ long, 24″ wide, and 29″ high, the table can also serve as a side table or even a cocktail table.

For more information, contact:

Dakota Jackson Inc.
306 E. 61st St.
New York, NY 10021
(212) 838-9444

hang from the four corners to tone down the bold geometry. Just who Nancy is we're not prepared to say.

For more information, contact:

Cyrna International
Space 12-101
The Merchandise Mart
Chicago, IL 60654
(312) 329-0906

BUTLER

Designed by Sottsass Associati, the Butler dumbwaiter is sturdy enough to take outdoors but attractive enough to use at indoor parties. Equipped with casters, the Butler rests on four thick legs available in black, gray, white, yellow, or red. The blue or black shelves are removable, as is the bottle rack. Framed with chrome tubing, the dumbwaiter measures 29¼″ by 30½″ by 19½″.

For further information, contact:

Gullans Henley International
227 W. 17th St.
New York, NY 10011
(212) 741-3384

NEW CLASSICS II BACKGAMMON TABLE

Dakota Jackson ingeniously makes the game board on his New Classics II backgammon table an integral part of the piece's overall design. The broad diamonds of inlaid burl give substance to the space between the black lacquered legs. The leather-coated wings have drawers. Measur-

FOLDING TROLLEY

Designer Louis Lucien Lepoix transforms sturdiness into elegance in his folding trolley. Manufactured by FRZ-Metallwarenfabrik in West Germany, it is offered by the Museum of Modern Art. The trolley measures 28½" by 15¾" by 23½", and folds into a width of only three inches, storing away excellently. The durable plastic coating, self-closing handles, and rotating wheels make it an ideal choice for serving food on the patio or in the house. Lepoix's trolley is available in white or black.

Catalogue, $2.

Mail Order Department
Museum of Modern Art
11 W. 53rd St.
New York, NY 10019
(212) 708-9888

DEMI LUNE CONSOLE

Donghia's Demi Lune entrance table will let newcomers to your home know immediately that you take interior design seriously. Brilliant patterned gold or silver leaf covers the broad tiers, and the fluted columns are coated with a black lacquer finish. The console measures 57" wide, 27" deep, and 32" high.

For further information, contact:

Donghia Furniture
485 Broadway
New York, NY 10013
(212) 925-2777

Beds

No single design trend embraces the modern bed. As the entries in this chapter demonstrate, beds can be mass produced or handmade and be equally contemporary and stylish. Experiments with the mattress—waterbeds or heart-shaped lits conjugaux—have plummeted into the abyss of sleaziness. Consequently, the beds presented here have conventional rectangular mattresses but boast variations on the bedstead—some practical and some ornamental. The effect can be monumental, as in Dakota Jackson's Art Deco bed, or intimate, as in the willow beds from La Lune or rattan ones from Willow & Reed. While the act of sleeping remains the same, its setting continues to change to fit the multifaceted fashions of the day.

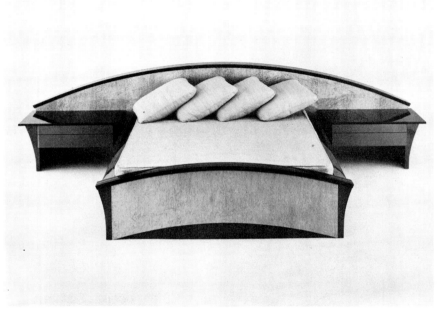

HALL TABLE AND MIRROR

The random patterns and clashing proportions of Bob Trotman's hall table and mirror might be called whimsical by some and New Wave by others. The wriggling legs of the table deliberately disturb the geometric serenity of the coordinated mirror and table top. The table measures 36″ wide and 15″ deep, and the mirror brings the height of the two pieces to 78″. The table and mirror are made of polychromed maple and mahogany with natural wood and black lacquer finishes.

For more information, contact:

Bob Trotman
Rt. 1, Box 100-A2
Casar, NC 28020
(704) 538-8236

ARC BED

Dakota Jackson enjoys combining gentle curves and straight lines in the designs of his furniture: the subtle dynamics between the two elements are quite absorbing. His Arc bed features a magnificent arcing headboard that stretches more than twelve feet across to embrace not only a full-sized mattress but two cantilevered night tables. The tables and footboard of the bed are gently curved as well. Made of lacquered bird's-eye maple and light and dark cherry, the piece measures 93″ deep and 36″ high at the headboard.

For further information, contact:

Dakota Jackson Inc.
306 E. 61st St.
New York, NY 10021
(212) 838-9444

JOLLA BED AND STB BED

The Children's Room offers a wide choice of beds that are handsome, but can withstand the onslaughts of budding trampoline artists.

The growth of children may be miraculous and wonderful, but it can become quite a burden on the parents' wallet. The extendible Jolla bed helps alleviate the problem; illustrated here, it measures 33″ wide, 16½″ high, and 53″ long—the right size for a young child. When the young child becomes a lanky teenager, the Jolla bed can slide out to 73″ in length, making it a bed that grows as the child does. An extra mattress section is provided. The Jolla bed comes in white with birch edges.

The STB bed, made of solid birch with a heavy finish, is an excellent improvement on the regular bunk bed arrangement. Both of the combinations in which the beds come feature a ladder to the top bunk, a bulletin board above the lower one, and planks that serve as shelving. The posts of the beds, cut in wide rectangles instead of weaker squares, have rounded corners to avoid painful late-night collisions. The STB is arranged either as a normal bunk bed with parallel bedsteads, or in an L-shape, the lower area housing a bed and a desk. The loft measures 80″ long, 40″ deep, and 67″ high.

Catalogue available.

The Children's Room
318 E. 45th St.
New York, NY 10017
(212) 687-3868

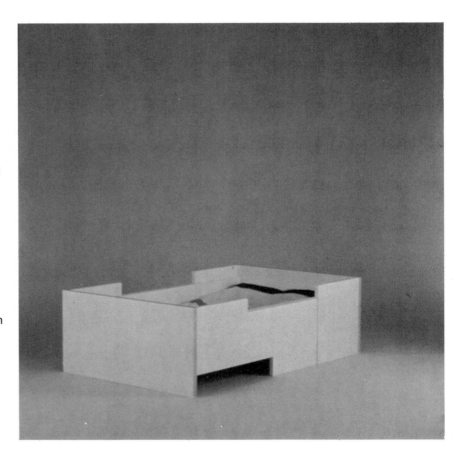

SUNBURST CRADLE

René Soulard makes wooden furniture of a uniquely personal design. The openings on the sides of Soulard's cradle take the form of carved silhouettes of sunbeams rather than gaps between prison bars. The different shades and rich grains of wood also add to the warm design that transforms the mundane into a work of art.

For more information about Soulard's work, contact:

René Soulard
1833 13th Ave., #208
Seattle, WA 98122
(206) 328-1164

LA LUNE WILLOW BED

La Lune specializes in willow furniture, reviving an ancient craft for the contemporary designer. The twin bed shown here is an example of the firm's work, with straight and curved willow branches forming the headboard and footboard as well as the bed frame. The willow bed shown measures 82″ long, 45″ wide, and 54″ high, but the design is also available in a king, queen, or full size, with or without the footboard.

For further information, contact:

La Lune Willow Collection
241 N. Broadway
Milwaukee, WI 53202
(414) 271-1172
- 414 - 263 - 5300 -

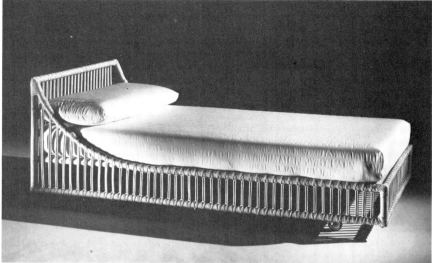

TIARA PLATFORM BED

The Tiara, by Willow & Reed, appears fresh and light in its simple rattan construction. A frame with a small elegant headboard supports the mattress, reinforced with hand-wrapped cane or leather bindings. The rattan, stripped of its bark, is available in an array of thirty-two different stained or lacquered finishes. The coordinated mattress cover also comes in thirty-two colors. Willow & Reed offers the Tiara in single, double, queen, and king sizes.

For further information, contact:

Willow & Reed
32-34 111th St.
East Elmhurst, NY 11539
(212) 335-0807

Chairs

While the holy tenets of functionalism have gone sour in other areas of interior design, they continue to invigorate the process of chair making. Designers, especially from Europe, continue to find innovative uses for steel tubing and plastics in the mass production of chairs.

Firms that specialize in replicating modern classic furniture also demonstrate the tenacity of functionalism: their catalogues offer a preponderance of chairs, such as Mies van der Rohe's cantilever and Le Corbusier's chaise longue. The philosophies of these early modern masters are particularly durable when applied to chair making; they currently show little loss of viability and probably never will.

Postmodernist designers are only beginning to approach chair making. Individual craftsmen offer imaginative works that feature highly figurative designs. Robert Venturi, one of the leaders of postmodernism, has recently designed a series of chairs for Knoll. While the chairs are witty and intellectually playful, they are mass produced and may therefore give some indication of where chair designs in general may go in the future.

LE CORBUSIER CHAISE LONGUE AND AALTO CHAISE

The pieces of furniture displayed in the Museum of Modern Art's Design Collection are some of the most beautiful and significant works of design of the century. Through the Museum Store, individuals can own replicas of these pieces as well.

The museum initiated the Le Corbusier Chaise into its Design Collection in 1950. Designed in 1927, the "cowboy chair" has few rivals to its elegant structure and dedication to human form. The black leather cushion is mounted on a contoured tubular chrome frame designed for optimum comfort. The curved rails under the seat rest on cylindrical rollers which thus allow the seated individual to tilt the chaise to a desired position. The entire assembly is supported by a strong four-legged subframe of painted steel. Made for the museum by Atelier International, Ltd., the chaise measures $62\frac{5}{16}$″ by $19\frac{9}{16}$″ by 24″.

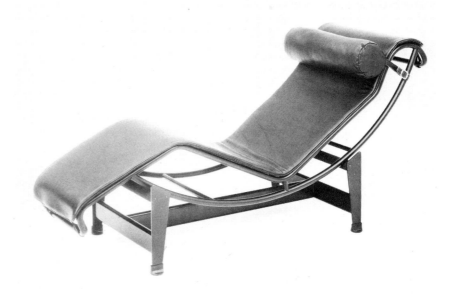

Alvar Aalto designed his chaise longue in 1937, but because of the difficulty involved in constructing it, its production was stopped soon afterwards. Artek of Finland, its manufacturer, issued a limited quantity of the chaises in 1982. The chair embodies Aalto's disdain for mechanized and metalized furniture; instead, Aalto shaped birchwood into flowing, almost organic, curves. The webbing for the chair is natural linen. The chaise longue, which measures $64\frac{1}{2}$″ long, 27″ high, and $25\frac{1}{2}$″ wide, is shown here with Aalto's fan-legged table and a Bauhaus lamp, also available from the museum's collection of modern classic furniture.

Catalogue, $2.

Mail Order Department
Museum of Modern Art
11 W. 53rd St.
New York, NY 10019
(212) 708-9888

BOULOUM

Olivier Mourgue designed the Bouloum chair in 1969, and its humorous, shadow-like form has been placed on permanent display at the Museum of Modern Art. The anthropormorphic chaise is available in fiberglass with a gel coating for outdoor use or steel tubing with upholstery for indoors. Wherever it is used, the Bouloum will set a casual tone. Measuring 26" wide, 57" deep, and 24" high, the upholstered chaise comes in twenty-nine different colors. The outdoor model measures 24" wide, 56" deep, and 23" high, with a white surface and black underside.

For further information, contact:

Arconas Corp.
580 Orwell St.
Mississauga, ONT L5A 3V7
Canada
(416) 272-0727

New York Showroom:

150 E. 58th St.
New York, NY 10022
(212) 753-4960

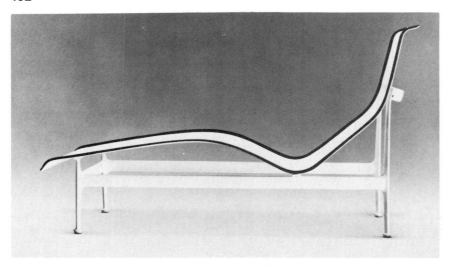

SCHULTZ CONTOUR CHAISE

Knoll has long been one of the premier makers of modern furniture, offering works of many masters of design. The Schultz Contour Chaise is an excellent example of Richard Schultz's careful attention to the human form. Reminiscent of Le Corbusier's cowboy chaise, Schultz's chair has an even more detailed curve to match a seated person's back and provides resilient comfort with a Dacron woven mesh sling. The frame is made of cast and extruded aluminum, and the entire chair measures 24½″ wide, 58″ long, and 33¾″ high.

For further information, contact:

Knoll International
The Knoll Building
655 Madison Ave.
New York, NY 10021
(212) 826-2400

TUB CHAIR

Falcon offers the plush, embracing chair shown here. Appropriate for any room meant for relaxing, the chair has a thick seat cushion, sloping armrests, and casters. It is also available with a pillow or split back.

For further information, contact:

Falcon Products Inc.
9387 Dielman Industrial Dr.
P.O. Box 21569
St. Louis, MO 63132
(314) 991-9200

Club and Lounge Chairs

5305 LOUNGE CHAIR

Thayer Coggin Institutional offers contemporary furniture, featuring fully upholstered pieces as well as chairs and sofas with wood or metal frames. Although designed to stand up to institutional use, T.C.I.'s furniture does well in the home, too. The lounge chair shown is a case in point. Designed by Milo Baughman, it has a beautifully unified look with a wraparound back. Several other models from Thayer Coggin Institutional have a similar style with casters or without feet.

For further information, contact:

Thayer Coggin Institutional, Inc.
P.O. Box 5867
High Point, NC 27262
(919) 880-1700

ANDROS

The almost over-stuffed back cushion, the over-sized hanging arm cushions, and the unusually wide size of the Andros chair all create the feeling and appearance of comfort. Imported by Axiom Designs, the Andros chair is made by Brunati of Italy. The cushions can be removed by means of zippers, and the metal frame is modular-constructed. The fabrics and leathers for this chair are available in a variety of colors.

For further information, contact:

Axiom Designs
110 Greene St.
New York, NY 10012
(212) 219-2212

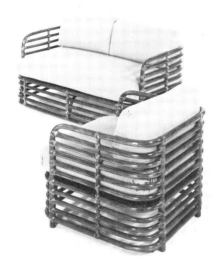

SOLARON

Solaron, unlike many other lines of outdoor furniture, emphasizes cushions rather than frames. The cushion is divided into three parts, with a contoured seat, a lower back pillow, and an upper back support. As with other Brown Jordan outdoor furniture, the Solaron chair and ottoman shown here are made with welded aluminum tubular framing, and the seats come in a range of bright colors.

Catalogue, $4.

Brown Jordan Co.
9860 Gidley St.
P.O. Box 5688
El Monte, CA 91734
(818) 443-8971

SCALA

Willow & Reed's rattan furniture permits you to enjoy plush, well-cushioned seating that can complement the often spare, light designs of modern interiors. The cushions on these armchairs and two-seat and three-seat settees are as generous as on any bulky sofa, and can come in a variety of upholstery materials, including the customer's own fabrics. The frames, though, are sets of well-spaced rows of rattan, bound with leather or cane. The rattan comes either stripped or with the bark intact.

For further information, contact:

Willow & Reed
32-34 111th St.
East Elmhurst, NY 11369
(718) 335-0807

ELAN LX LOUNGE CHAIR

Working with the Brown Jordan design, Jeff Cronk has designed a series of outdoor furniture, which, while certainly attractive, is unquestionably durable. Show here is the Elan LX lounge chair, the frame of which features oval aluminum extrusion with heliarc welding at the joints. The lounge chair measures 26½" wide and 33" long, and stands 15½" high.

A matching ottoman is available.

Catalogue, $4.

Brown Jordan Co.
9860 Gidley St.
Box 5688
El Monte, CA 91734
(818) 443-8971

T-LINE

A quantum leap above ordinary self-assembled furniture, Beylerian's T-line is easy to put together and has a very contemporary look. Available in either leather or fabric, the T-line comes as a low-back or a high-back. The high-back comes with an optional headrest.

For further information, contact:

Beylerian
305 E. 63rd St.
New York, NY 10021
(212) 755-6300

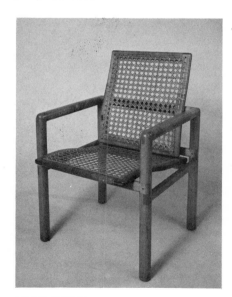

CANE CHAIR

Chairs built for the way we ought to sit generally place us at military attention. George Berry builds his cane chair instead to the way in which we

like to sit—slouching. The chair's back pivots on the armrests to follow the movement of the sitter's back. Hand-carved, the chair is pegged together rather than nailed. It measures 34″ high and 22″ wide.

For further information, contact:

George Berry
745 Edgewood Ave., N.E.
Atlanta, GA 30307
(404) 577-4433

WING CHAIR III

Only the most ambitious designer should try to incorporate Robert Chehayl's Wing Chair III into a room scheme; in a normal household it will overpower every other piece of furniture. Cut from beefwood, a dense tropical wood, the chair offers a cavity for a person to ensconce himself in the powerful sculpture. Chehayl mounts the chair on a mauve-colored base of soft maple and gives it a final touch with neon lights under the wings. This amazing sitting experience measures 23½″ high, 35″ wide, and 103″ long.

For further information, contact:

Robert Chehayl
49 Harrison St.
Hoboken, NJ 07030
(201) 798-3018

193 RECLINER

Curved sides on this recliner are an attractive alternative to chubby conventional models. Made by Thayer Coggin, the chair measures 34″ wide, 37″ deep, and 38″ high. It can assume three comfortable positions.

Catalogue, $4.

Thayer Coggin Inc.
427 South Rd.
P.O. Box 5867
High Point, NC 27262
(919) 889-1700

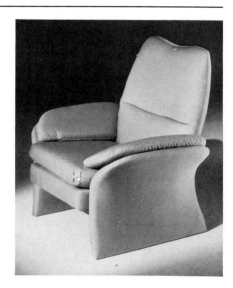

PAIMIO CHAIR

When Alvar Aalto introduced his Paimio chair in 1931, it was hailed as the first "soft wooden chair." Aalto derived this unique effect by bending a piece of plywood and then resting it on ribbons of birch that serve as the frame, legs, and arms of the chair. The Paimio chair thus has a resilient spring to it. The Museum of Modern Art placed Aalto's chair in its Design Collection in 1943 and offers replicas through the Museum Store. Artek of Finland makes the chair with molded plywood and laminated birch with a black enamel finish. The chair measures 25½" by 24" by 34". Also shown here are the Museum Store's Aalto stacking stools and an Eileen Gray lamp. All rest on a Juan Gris wool rug.

Catalogue, $2.

Mail Order Department
Museum of Modern Art
11 W. 53rd. St.
New York, NY 10019
(212) 708-9888

SCULTURA CHAIR

Designer Nicola Trussardi gives the cushioning of the Scultura the precise angles and unity you would expect from a chair made of steel. Seemingly cut from a single block of material, the chair is covered with natural cowhide and, over it, Crespo—a synthetic material available in yellow, black, red, or white. A chair of unusual comfort,

Scultura is made for Scalia and measures 39″ wide, 29½″ deep, and 35″ high.

For further information, contact:

The Greenbaum Collection
101 Washington St.
Paterson, NJ 07505
(201) 279-3000

down-lined core of polyurethane foam. The armchairs measure 41½″ wide, 33″ deep, and 30″ high, with a seat height of 18″. The headrest is an option on both the armchair and the matching sofa.

For more information, contact:

The Greenbaum Collection
101 Washington St.
Paterson, NJ 07505
(201) 279-3000

JEFF KELLAR

One can draw a smooth line from furniture builders of earlier periods to Jeff Kellar. "I look to the styles of the past," he explains, "not for direct quotation in the postmodernist vein, but in hope of distilling some of the spirit that animates them." By way of illustration, Kellar's lounge chair, shown here, clearly displays the revitalized elements of traditional craftsmanship without its clichés. Made of East Indian rosewood, it is upholstered with mohair and measures 31″ high, 26″ deep, and 28½″ wide.

For further information about the designer's work, contact:

Jeff Kellar
P.O. Box 4770
Portland, ME 04112
(207) 773-6269

DERBY

Armchairs from Nicola Trussardi's collection of furniture bring the height of comfort to their owners without sacrificing a handsome appearance. By limiting the frame of the Derby arm-

chair to only a curved L, Trussardi keeps a seated person surrounded by cushions—uniquely handsome cushions made of calf leather with stripes of polished leather and stuffed with a

TUX STACKING CHAIR

Haigh Space, Ltd., designs the Tux stacking chair so sparingly that the bareness becomes, paradoxically, ornamental. The tubular steel frame extends like insect legs from the seat and is braced at several points. The

NEW YORK TUB CHAIR

Donghia's New York tub chairs provide luxurious comfort at the home or in the office. Their long, sloping arms and thick cushions are upholstered in a wool-cord weave, but can also be upholstered in a variety of other fabrics. The Art Deco legs come in an assortment of finishes; brass casters or a swivel base are also available.

The chair comes in two sizes: 34" wide, 36" deep, and 33" high; or 33" wide, 33" deep, and 31" high..

For further information, contact:

Donghia Furniture
485 Broadway
New York, NY 10013
(212) 925-2777

seat and back are made of folded sheet steel, available with or without perforations. The chair comes in black, red, yellow, light green, or white, with a gray frame. Measuring 19" by 19" by 29½", the Tux chair comes with a matching stacking table.

For further information, contact:

Gullan Henley International
227 W. 17th St.
New York, NY 10011
(212) 741-3384

ARM LOUNGE CHAIR

While casual in appearance, this lounge chair by Falcon is quite sturdy. A sled base and contoured seat and back all ensure a long life for the chair and comfort for the user. Made of beechwood, the lounge chair is available in a wide variety of finishes and upholstery.

For more information, contact:

Falcon Products Inc.
9387 Dielman Industrial Dr.
P.O. Box 21569
St. Louis, MO 63132
(314) 991-9200

MALLET-STEVENS STACKING CHAIR

Palazzetti offers the public a large collection of classic modern furniture—chairs, tables, and couches—that students of design recognize immediately. The work of Robert Mallet-Stevens is featured in the collection, including his 1930 stacking chair, created for the kitchen of the Villa Carvoiz in Croix, France. The chairs do not have the uncompromising rationalism of works of Le Corbusier; while they are spare and refined, they still demonstrate an unmodernistic concern for beautiful form which is not specifically intended for efficiency. Available in gray, black, red, or blue, the chair measures 17¾" by 20½" by 32" and is made of steel tubing and sheet steel.

Catalogue, $15.

Palazzetti, Inc.
215 Lexington Ave.
New York, NY 10016
(212) 684-1199

REGISTA CHAIR

The Regista chair is eminently portable. Weighing less than five pounds, the metal frame collapses easily on itself, the canvas back and seat folding away unobtrusively. The chair will not twist or buckle like other folding chairs because of the sturdy construction and well-designed cross braces. Measuring 31" high and 20" deep, it folds out from 4" to 20". The canvas seat and back come in three combinations of colors. Once again, the Pottery Barn proves that good modern design needn't be expensive.

The Pottery Barn has 28 branch stores. For further information, contact:

The Pottery Barn
175 Clearbrook Rd.
Elmsford, NY 10523
(914) 592-2330

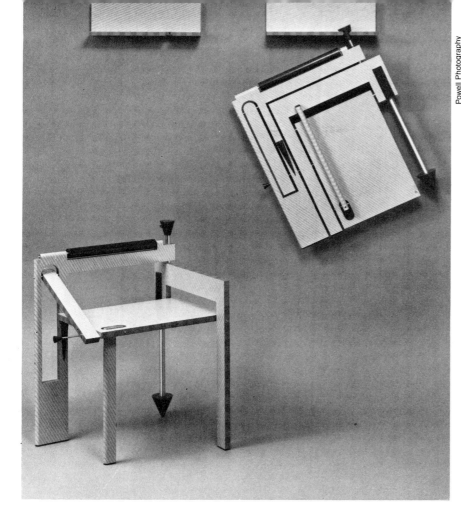

Powell Photography

FOLDING CHAIR

Tom Loeser transforms the mechanistic nature of modern furniture into sculpture. Illustrated is his folding chair, an occasional chair which collapses into a puzzle of wooden panels and metal hinges. Even hanging from its own rack, it is a work of art. Measuring 27" by 25" by 24" when unfolded, the chair is typical of Loeser's one-of-a-kind furniture available through galleries or directly by commission.

For further information, contact:

Tom Loeser
16 Emily St.
Cambridge, MA 02139
(617) 661-9836

UNFOLDING CHAIR

In trying to humanize the folding chair, Peter Danko has ended up making it immensely simpler and more efficient. The molded plywood provides excellent back support and collapses on pliable material instead of hinges. 31" high, 20" wide, and 22" deep when open, Danko's chair folds down to a 2" depth. It is available with or without foam cushioning.

For further information about this and other original Danko designs, contact:

Peter Danko & Associates Inc.
7492-F Old Alexander Ferry Rd.
Clinton, MD 20735
(301) 292-1653

PLANO

Available in either oak or cherry wood, Plano stacking chairs are one of Lübke's impressive assaults against the rickety discomfort of group seating. The solid-wood frame comes with arms as shown here or without, and both models can be stacked together. Designed by Harmut Elberfeld, these chairs can be complemented by other matching pieces of furniture from Lübke.

For more information, contact:

Lübke International Design
P.O. Box 4795
High Point, NC 27263
(919) 884-8042

Or in Canada:

c/o Pieter Schat
P.O. Box 202, Stn. M
299 Glenlake Ave.
Toronto, ONT M6S 4T3
Canada
(416) 769-0812

ION STACK CHAIRS

With the design of his Ion stack chairs, Norman Cherner succeeds in adding the efficiency of stacking to the handsomeness of his other furniture. The rectangular legs curve into elegantly rolled edges, and the rounded back is positioned low so as to provide an arresting design as well as lower back support. Ion chairs are available in oak, cherry, walnut, mahogany, or maple, each in a variety of oil and lacquer finishes. They stack into groups of six.

For further information, contact:

Modern Mode, Inc.
111 San Leandro Blvd.
San Leandro, CA 94577
(415) 568-6650

PARCO

The wide range of design options for the Parco stacking chair make it an excellent choice for handsome, easily stored furniture. The upholstered parts of the chair are interchangeable, and the chair itself, made of beech, is available in side chair and armchair models. The back comes either fully or partially upholstered in any of Lübke's large selection of covering materials.

For further information, contact:

Lübke International Design
P.O. Box 4795
High Point, NC 27263
(919) 884-8042

Or in Canada:

Lübke International Design
c/o Pieter Schat
P.O. Box 202, Stn. M
299 Glenlake Ave.
Toronto, ONT M6S 4T3
Canada
(416) 769-0812

INTEGRA

Tough, resilient, sturdy—the Integra chairs are the Marines of the contemporary design world. They can be abused to no end; their manufacturer, the Norix Group, boasts that they simply will not break or crack. Integra chairs are made of polypropylene, a rigid yet flexible and lightweight material. The chairs can be used indoors or outdoors and are excellent for large seatings: they are designed to fit snugly into rows and can be stacked as well.

Brochure available.

Norix Group, Inc.
P.O. Box 298
Batavia, IL 60510-0298
(312) 879-6160

BLITZ

Designer Motomi Kawakami makes his Blitz folding chairs attractive and comfortable without sacrificing ease of portability. Blitz's seat and back are strengthened by metal bands covered in polyurethane foam. The steel legs come in either black or chrome.

For further information, contact:

Innovative Products for Interiors,
  Inc.
315 E. 62nd St.
New York, NY 10021
(212) 838-2900

PETER DANKO ROCKER

Drawing much of his inspiration from Thonet's 19th-century rocking chair, Peter Danko deftly combines simplicity and liveliness in the design. The rockers appear to be bending, spring-like, as if under a weight. The chair measures 38″ high, 27½″ wide, and 38″ deep. Made of solid laminated oak, ash, walnut, and cherry, the rockers and arms feature pinned and doweled joinery. The seat, more plush than that of most rocking chairs, is made of a plywood core with foam cushioning.

For further information, contact:

Peter Danko & Associates Inc.
7492-F Old Alexander Ferry Rd.
Clinton, MD 20735
(301) 292-1653

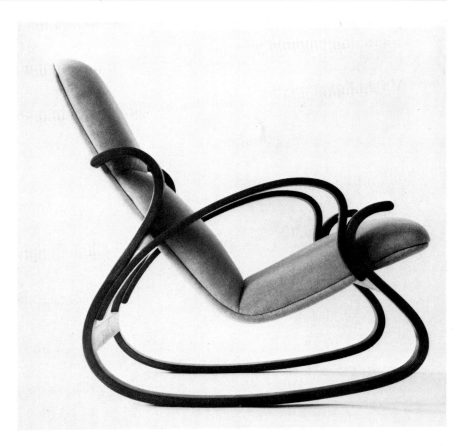

TOM WESSELLS ROCKER

Tom Wessells builds just about every conceivable piece of wood furniture as one-of-a-kind commissions. Wessells' graceful rocker is constructed of oil-finished white oak with Nicaraguan rosewood in a bent lamination process. The long rockers provide smooth oscillation, and the gently curved slats ensure a comfortable seat. The chair measures 36″ by 30″ by 40″.

For further information, contact:

Tom Wessells
4 Graham Dr.
Newport News, VA 23606
(804) 599-5615

CHEHAYL ROCKER

It is a long, long way from the Boston rockers of our grandparents to Robert Chehayl's rocking chair. The straight and bent sections of the rockers complement the exotic shape of the seat and its rich streaked maple back. The rockers form free-standing armrests. Chehayl's rocking chair measures 34" high, 31" wide, and 37" deep.

For further information, contact:

Robert Chehayl
49 Harrison St.
Hoboken, NJ 07030
(201) 798-3018

LEAF ROCKER

Even while retaining the conventional design of a rocking chair, René Soulard transforms this piece of traditional American furniture into an exotic object. Fleshy leaves decorate the back and sides of Soulard's rocker and the entire work is carved out of Koa, a deep, fine-grained Hawaiian wood. It measures 48″ high and 24″ across.

For further information, contact:

René Soulard
1833 13th Ave., #208
Seattle, WA 98122
(206) 328-1164

Side Chairs and Armchairs

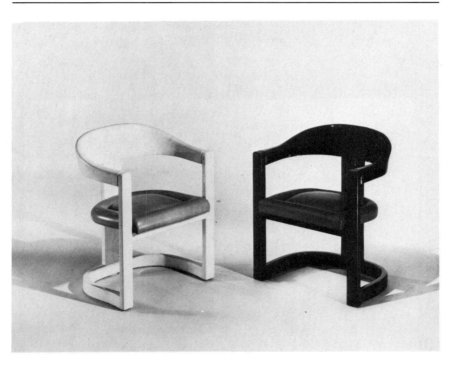

CONTEMPORARY SIDE CHAIR

Casa Stradivari is particularly proud of its recent introduction of "Jewel-Tone" lacquers. Brilliant metallic shades—among them sapphire, ruby, moonstone, emerald, amethyst, tan opal, and sunstone—are complemented by equally bold fabrics. The combination of ebony silk and moonstone lacquer is shown in the side chair illustrated here. The structure of the chair—strong lines without any wasteful additions—contributes even further to its arresting appearance. It stands 35″ high and is 18″ wide and 21½″ deep.

For more information, contact:

Casa Stradivari
200 Lexington Ave.
New York, NY 10016
(212) 684-5990

ONASSIS CHAIRS

Onassis chairs consist only of a curved frame with two slats to support the seat, thus displaying, in a matter of speaking, a certain elegant absence. Springer offers these chairs in a number of finishes, including goatskin or black lacquer as shown here. They are available through architects, designers, and specifiers.

For further information, contact:

Karl Springer, Ltd.
306 E. 61st St.
New York, NY 10021
(212) 752-1695

HALO CHAIR

Beylerian's Halo chair displays a symmetry that is so intense that it becomes a beautiful element of design in itself. Available in a polyvinyl or textured finish, the Halo chair can be used outdoors as well as indoors.

For more information, contact:

Beylerian
305 E. 63rd St.
New York, NY 10021
(212) 755-6300

CONTATTO CHAIR

The Contatto series, made in Italy by Brunati and imported by Axiom Designs, includes sofas, chairs, and footstools. The molded polyurethane cushions of the side chair shown here are stuffed with goose down and are tailor-upholstered; thus a handsome chair becomes a quite comfortable one. The metal frame is available in a range of color finishes.

For further information, contact:

Axiom Designs
110 Greene St.
New York, NY 10012
(212) 219-2212

P85 ARMCHAIR

Part of Origlia's Wood and Lacquers Collection of furniture, the P85 Armchair has not only the lightness of a Thonet bentwood chair, but solemnity as well, making it appropriate for formal occasions. The wood can be lacquered in black, white, gray, or burgundy, and the upholstery is available in a range of fabrics.

For further information, contact:

Origlia USA Inc.
200 Lexington Ave.
New York, NY 10016
(212) 532-0075

166

MR CHAIR

Palazzetti offers Mies van der Rohe's 1927 MR armchair upholstered in wicker or leather. Made of mirror-polished chrome-plated steel tubes, the frame demonstrates Mies van der Rohe's innovative exposure of metal, an aesthetic preference which has never really gone out of style. The seat and armrests of the wicker chair are made of hand-woven natural cane. The leather chair comes in a variety of colors. Both chairs measure 32½″ deep, 21″ wide, and 31″ high.

Catalogue, $15.

Palazzetti, Inc.
215 Lexington Ave.
New York, NY 10016
(212) 684-1199

DINING CHAIR

A sophisticated fabric back panel insert is a handsome feature of this dining room chair from Falcon. Made of beech, the chair comes in a variety of wood finishes and upholstery. The elegantly curved back can be replaced with a double wooden slat back or a full upholstered inset.

For further information, contact:

Stendig, Inc.
410 E. 62nd St.
New York, NY 10021
(212) 838-6050

ANDOVER

Seventeenth-century Windsor chairs made use of spindles as lightweight back supports. Davis Allen extends them to the arms of his Andover armchair to make further use of their beautiful form. A magnificent effect results as the strong pattern of vertical black lines opposes the broad width of the seat. Andover is part of the New American Furniture Classics collection offered by Stendig, and comes also as a side chair. Both models are available with woven cane seats.

For more information, contact:

Falcon Products Inc.
9387 Dielman Industrial Dr.
P.O. Box 21569
St. Louis, MO 63132
(314) 991-9200

Designed in 1900, the chair is dynamic enough to remain viable in a contemporary home. One slender bentwood rod forms the legs and back and another the arms. The seat is a latticework of woven cane. Corbusier's namesake, offered through the Museum of Modern Art, measures 28¾″ by 20⅞″ by 21¹⁵⁄₁₆″.

Catalogue, $2.

Mail Order Department
Museum of Modern Art
11 W. 53rd St.
New York, NY 10019
(212) 708-9888

HAARLEM II AND VERONDA CHAIR

As the two chairs shown here demonstrate, Interna Designs offers some of the most innovative furniture available. The Haarlem II chair from Peter Miles Furniture of England almost looks too postmodern to be at all practical, and yet it is a comfortable, sturdy dining chair. Designer Ronald Carter gives the chair its imbalanced, strangely proportioned shape by simply sloping the back slats and enlarging the seat. It measures 36″ high, 16¾″ wide, and 21½″ deep.

Made by Ferro Nuovo and offered by Interna Designs, the Veronda chair is a witty study in illusions. A single ⅝″ solid rod of steel forms the frame of the chair, passing through the back which seems to levitate. Designed by architect George Veronda, the chair is

uncharacteristically strong. Fabrics and finishes can be coordinated in a wide assortment of combinations.

For further information, contact:

Interna Designs, Ltd.
Space 6-168
The Merchandise Mart
Chicago, IL 60654
(312) 467-6076

CORBUSIER CHAIR 6009

Le Corbusier did not like much that came before him, but he did like nineteenth-century Thonet chairs. He even furnished his Pavillon de l'Esprit Nouveau exhibit in 1925 solely with the German bentwood chairs. Thonet still makes this chair in its American factory, calling it the Corbusier chair.

Paul Aresu

D-ARM CHAIR

Anyone who doubts the versatility of acrylic as a medium of interior design will become a true believer when sitting in Plexability's D-Arm chair. This unusual chair displays to advantage broad, rounded half arches of acrylic, which form its arms and legs, and the upholstered back forms a coordinated full arch. Measuring 31″ high, 18″ wide, and 19″ deep, the chair comes upholstered in a variety of fabrics.

For further information, contact:

Plexability
New York Design Building
Suite 506
200 Lexington Ave.
New York, NY 10016
(212) 679-7826

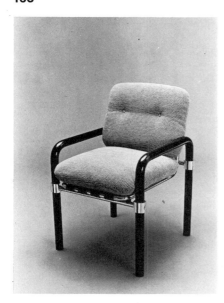

PIPE LINE 3 ECLIPSE EDITION

Onyx-black cast-acrylic rods, given a mirror-like finish, make for a captivating chair. The Pipe Line 3 Eclipse dining chair from Jeff Messerschmidt also has a stainless-steel frame, hand-polished aluminum extrusions, and saddle leather straps. By casting acrylic, Messerschmidt does not merely surface these rods in black, but saturates the material with the color.

For further information, contact:

Jeff Messerschmidt Designs
P.O. Box 382
Dallas, GA 30132
(404) 942-5949

CIRCA

The Circa chair, through its singular construction, eliminates the need for upholstery. Long slender spindles of laminated beechwood, treated for elasticity and tensility, give a little when leaned on and thus act like a cushion for the sitter. They bow outward as well to lend lower back support. These lightweight chairs, capable of serving a range of needs, are comfortable enough for the family room and formal enough for the dining room. They measure 28½″ high and have 20½″-diameter seats.

For more information, contact:

Lübke International Design
P.O. Box 4795
High Point, NC 27263
(919) 884-8042

Or in Canada:

Lübke International Design
C/o Pieter Schat
P.O. Box 202, Stn. M
299 Glenlake Ave.
Toronto, ONT M6S 4T3
Canada
(416) 769-0812

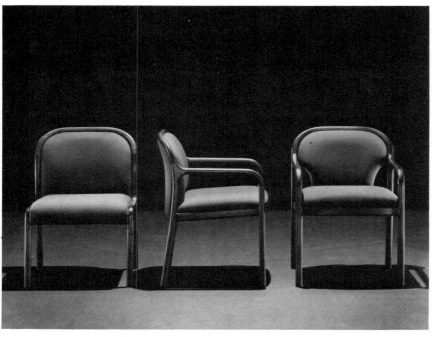

WESTPORT COLLECTION CHAIRS

The chairs in Norman Cherner's Westport collection have a frame design that seems almost human in the way it flows from arms to legs to seat. The chairs are available in oak, walnut, mahogany, ash, or cherry, with a variety of oil and lacquer finishes. The Westport collection includes side chairs and armchairs with variously shaped back panels, as well as armchairs with casters.

For further information, contact:

Modern Mode, Inc.
111 San Leandro Blvd.
San Leandro, CA 94577
(415) 568-6650

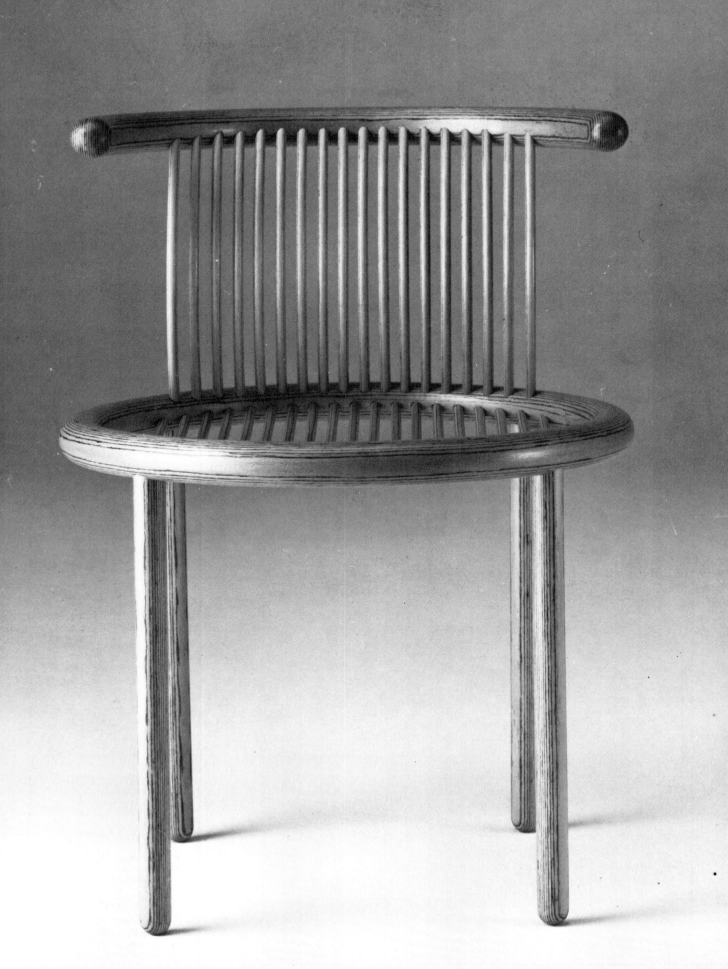

LOTUSBACK

Peter Danko's Lotusback chair is part of the Everychair series, a group of chairs united by a graceful simplicity of design. Made of molded plywood, the chair measures 32″ high, 22″ wide, and 21″ deep. The back fans out at the top and the frame has sloping supports which curve gently out to the sides to match the back. The polyurethane foam cushioning is available in a range of upholstery; the wood, in a number of finishes.

For further information, contact:

Peter Danko & Associates Inc.
7492-F Old Alexander Ferry Rd.
Clinton, MD 20735
(301) 292-1653

STRATEX 100, WOOD BENCH, AND ART CHAIR

Cyrna International offers furniture and accessories from some of the most progressive designers. The Stratex 100 series of chairs is well-suited to a number of environments, including offices, dining rooms, and game rooms. Designed by Dennis Christiansen, Stratex chairs have double-stitched back panels, tight seat construction, and either sculpted wood or lacquer-finished front legs. The Stratex 100 line is available as both side chairs and armchairs, the latter having either closed or open panels.

While Art Chair may seem to have a perfectly presumptuous name, it is what it says it is—a work of art. Playing with form and line, Jeff Lederman has created an interesting combina-

tion of lines and curves kept in tight symmetry. The Art Chair is steadfast and handy. Made of lacquered wood, the matte-black seat and legs have an industrial-strength finish. The back is finished in a high-gloss turquoise.

For further information about these and other Cyrna pieces, contact:

Cyrna International
The Merchandise Mart
Space 12-101
Chicago, IL 60654
(312) 329-0906

Some chairs are so contemporary that it takes a while to determine that they are in fact chairs and not merely *objets d'art*. Such is the shock of the new—in this case, the striking furniture design of Jeff Lederman. Seen at first as a classic Roman chair gone modern, the lacquered wood bench proves to be an efficient use of space as a two-sided, sturdy seat well worth admiring and owning.

KAILUA

The sleigh-runner shape of these lawn chairs works especially well on such soft outdoor surfaces as grass and sand. Designed by Hall Bradley for Brown Jordan, the Kailua series of furniture includes the lounge chairs shown here and five other pieces of furniture. The chairs measure 24" wide and 26½" deep, and they stand 15¼" high.

Catalogue, $4.

Brown Jordan Co.
9860 Gidley St.
P.O. Box 5688
El Monte, CA 91734
(818) 443-8971

VENTURI COLLECTION CHAIRS

Postmodernist furniture is probably the most intellectual of all; the subtle, joking allusions to very specific styles from the past may force owners of such pieces to buy a furniture encyclopedia. Robert Venturi's collection of chairs, sofas, and tables draws on historical styles ranging from the Middle Ages to the present. Postmodernism does not mean simple reproduction, however; Venturi adds freakish modifications and jarring modernizations that turn his furniture into witty puns. The Chippendale chair shown here, for example, has the interweaving back elements and curved ornamentation of Thomas Chippendale's pieces, but these details are bloated and simplified. Seen from the front, Venturi's chair gives the impression of stately massiveness. But, as the side view shows, it is actually made of bentwood laminations which are amazingly thin. The chair measures 25½″ wide, 23¼″ deep, and 37⅜″ high.

The Art Deco chair (left) and the Sheraton chair (right) have similar designs. The Sheraton displays the hallmarks of the late-eighteenth-century English style as well as a contrasting cartoon-like hand-screened illumination of a vase. A few perforations evoke the 1930s on Venturi's Art Deco chair and are similarly juxtaposed with a discordant pattern. Both of these chairs are made of bentwood laminations. The Sheraton measures 23⅛″ wide, 23⅞″ deep, and 33½″ high; the Art Deco chair, 23½″ wide, 23⅞″ deep, and 31¾″ high.

For further information, contact:

Knoll International
The Knoll Building
655 Madison Ave.
New York, NY 10021
(212) 826-2400

DESKS

The desks presented here are unusual but practical alternatives to the conventional box-shaped model. You might think that their strange shapes would squeeze out the efficiency a desk is supposed to have, but you'd be wrong. As much as some may look like letters of the alphabet or beasts from the jungle, all of these desks still supply an ample working surface, plenty of drawers, and sufficient leg room, not to mention a surplus of artistic imagination.

T-BIRD '56 DESK

Transplanting the sharp angles of a Thunderbird to a desk is a risky operation, but Dakota Jackson succeeds in capturing the spirit of the '50s automobile. The base, a lacquered wedge, has a cavity for leg room and two drawers on one side. The ½"-thick glass top is supported by aluminum rods with anodized heads and steel cables. The entire desk measures 84" wide, 30" deep, and 30" high.

For further information, contact:

**Dakota Jackson Inc.
306 E. 61st St.
New York, NY 10021
(212) 838-9444**

TECHNOLINEA

Origlia has stripped the desk down to its most basic features: a large, flat writing area with two nearly invisible drawers. The dramatic T-shaped Technolinea shown here in rosewood, is also available in walnut, oak, and bird's-eye maple. It measures 86½" long, 39½" wide, and 30" high.

For more information, contact:

**Origlia USA Inc.
200 Lexington Ave.
New York, NY 10016
(212) 532-0075**

TOM WESSELLS DESK

The common-sense sensibility of Tom Wessells' desk seems an odd partner to its distinctly contemporary and un-traditional appearance. The construction combines the legs, drawers, and writing space in a unified design. The desk is made of birch with details in other woods and measures 40″ by 30″ by 36″.

Tom Wessells executes one-of-a-kind commissions of virtually any kind of furniture.

For more information, contact:

Tom Wessells
4 Graham Dr.
Newport News, VA 23606
(804) 599-5615

POWELL DESK

David Powell's desk may seem at first sight to be outlandish and impractical, but its imaginative design actually is very efficient and logical. The main body, with the lid closed, is quite compact—only 22″ deep—permitting the desk to fit in small spaces. Without any low drawers on either side, the desk offers unlimited leg room while not sacrificing any storage room. It has fifteen drawers and ribbed cubbyholes made of satin-wood. The writing surface is lux-uriously lined with matched pieces of Moroccan goatskin, and the case is covered in cowhide. Mounted on a pair of braced maple legs, the desk measures 54″ wide and 54″ high.

For further information, contact:

Powell & Tierney Furniture
1 College St.
Easthampton, MA 07027
(413) 527-4952

COFFEY DESK AND CHAIR

In his New Hampshire workshop, Michael Coffey and several apprentices build one-of-a-kind furniture pieces for interior designers and individual customers. The desk and chair shown here rebel against conventional preoccupations with symmetry and standard angles. Both pieces are made of Mozambique, an exotic wood. The desk measures 44″ wide, 30″ deep, and 39″ high and has one large drawer under the working surfaces and two smaller ones with cubbyholes in the upper curve. The chair measures 21″ wide, 18″ deep, and 18″ high.

For further information about this and other Coffey designs, contact:

Michael Coffey
River Rd.
West Lebanon, NH 03784
(603) 298-8124

OBELISK DESK

Joseph Valerio ignores convention in the creation of his obelisk desk, a capricious construction including an unaccompanied corner obelisk in mottled gray. The center support and top panel have Colorcore surfacing, notable for coloring which flows through the entire material, thus eliminating black bordering. The ladder-like triangular side supports are made of metal with an epoxy finish. The desk measures 30″ in height, 60″ in width, and 30″ in depth.

For more information about this and other pieces from Valerio's Milwaukee Collection, contact:

Maville Interiors
200 Lexington Ave.
New York, NY 10016
(212) 689-3662 or (212) 684-3662

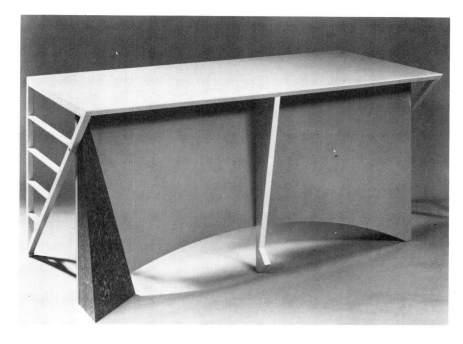

DESK

Jere Osgood has designed an unusual desk for Pritam & Eames, preserving conventional working efficiency within a design that seems as wily as a jungle animal. Deep Brazilian rosewood forms the main section, and the supports and drawers are made of ash. A leather blotter provides a wide writing area.

For further information, contact:

Pritam & Eames
29 Race Lane
East Hampton, NY 11937
(516) 324-7111

NEW CLASSICS DESK

The innovations in Dakota Jackson's desk design do not abandon classic proportions or make the desk awkward. A plate glass top, ½"-thick, serves as an efficient work surface, and the two drawers are completely enclosed to preserve privacy. The bent cherry legs and lacquered wings with metal caps form an arc, characteristic of the entire New Classics series. The desk measures 72" wide, 32" deep, and 29" high.

For further information, contact:

Dakota Jackson Inc.
306 E. 61st St.
New York, NY 10021
(212) 838-9444

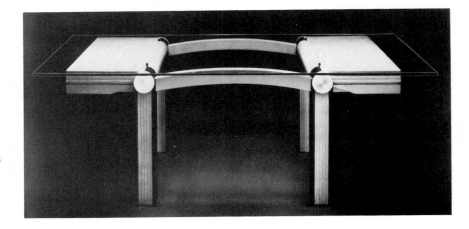

Storage and Shelving

Units used for storage must be functional, but they can also be attractive additions to the home. All of the systems and pieces displayed in the following pages—whether mass-produced or individually crafted—share *these twin virtues. Well-designed, intelligent constructions of shelves, wire baskets, and modular cabinets are ideal for those swamped by possessions, whether in large quarters or small. Less streamlined in style, but no* *less efficient as storage space, are the intricately constructed cabinets, chests, and armoires by various craftsmen.*

BRAZILIAN ARMOIRE AND PARTITION CABINET

George Berry's one-of-a-kind pieces of furniture are exceptional. His armoire, for example, is a massive, meticulously crafted object. The modules are made of black walnut, and the front panels, vacuum-formed into concave curves, consist of Brazilian rosewood over Italian bent poplar. Inside is an assortment of drawers made of Baltic birch and lined with leather. And to be sure to protect the product of four months' painstaking labor, Berry has coated the armoire with nine layers of hand-rubbed oil.

The capacity of a Berry storage system can be as impressive as its appearance. The cabinet shown here measures 12' by 3' by 9' and performs services that would otherwise require many individual pieces of furniture. Designed to divide a living room from a kitchen, the cabinet features on one side sufficient space for a television, VCR, home computer, video cassette rack, stereo speakers, and record bin. On the kitchen side, the black-lacquered bar plywood cabinet contains a built-in folding breakfast table, a kitchen telephone desk, a china closet, a linen closet, and sufficient room for other appliances. With all these features, Berry has also managed to fit in another 150 cubic feet of storage space to suit individual needs.

For further information about this fine craftsman's work, contact:

George Berry
745 Edgewood Ave. N.E.
Atlanta, GA 30307
(404) 577-4433

WALNUT CABINET AND ROSEWOOD CABINET

In addition to supplying manufacturers with prototypes for mass-produced furniture, John Kapel makes custom furniture. As can be seen, such individual work could never be mass produced. The wall-hung cabinet shown here consists of curving strips of walnut that swirl up into knoblike projections. The cabinet measures 24″ by 42″ by 10″, but, as Kapel notes, no two of his custom works are the same.

In this second example of Kapel's alternatives to bland, impassive cabinets, the designer cuts pieces of

NEW CLASSICS ARMOIRE

The New Classics Armoire is a fine example of the continuing revival of Art Deco design. Standing 84″ high and 54″ wide, it displays immense columns, arcs, and marble crown caps. Bird's-eye maple doors are set in a light cherry frame with lacquer molding and handles. Dakota Jackson offers the armoire with three choices of interiors—with rods and shelves, rods and drawers, or drawers and pull-out accommodations for televisions or stereos.

For further information, contact:

Dakota Jackson Inc.
306 E. 61st St.
New York, NY 10021
(212) 838-9444

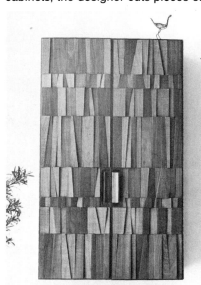

rosewood with a band saw and fits them together in the form of doors, giving the cabinet a beautiful topography. The wall-hung cabinet measures 24″ by 42″ by 10″.

For further information about Kapel's handcrafted work, contact:

John Kapel
80 Skywood Way
Woodside, CA 94062
(415) 851-0888

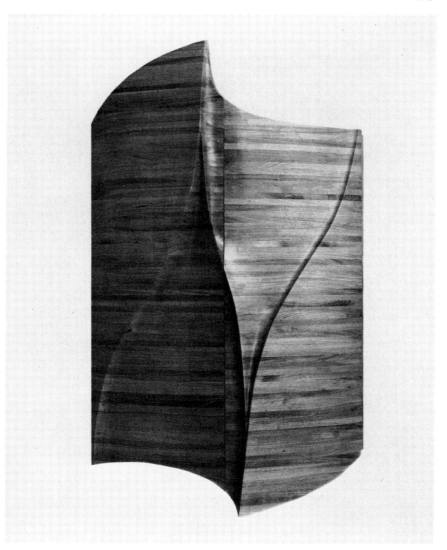

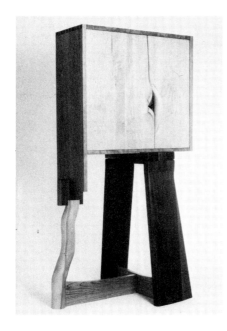

HIGHBOY

Much of Tom Wessells' work creates a tension between the formality of conventional furniture-making and the lush irregularity of unmanipulated wood. His highboy, for example, has precisely cut angles on its frame, but the form is disturbed by a knot in the cherry-wood doors and by a wriggling leg. The base is made of walnut and maple, and the entire piece measures 50″ high, 30″ wide, and 24″ deep.

For further information about Wessells' designs, contact:

Tom Wessells
4 Graham Dr.
Newport News, VA 23606
(804) 599-5615

OVATION

For artisans such as Michael Coffey, even the Modernists are old-fashioned, concerned as they are with symmetry, efficiency, and industrial assembly. Ovation, his courageously individualistic wall cabinet, demonstrates his love for hitherto unexplored regions of curves, crests, and depths that utilitarian furniture was not allowed to enjoy before. Made of laminated butternut, Ovation is designed to house stereo components and 150 records. It measures 47″ wide, 29″ deep, and 80″ high.

For further information about this and other Coffey designs, contact:

Michael Coffey
River Rd.
West Lebanon, NH 03784
(603) 298-8124

180

RADIANT BUFFET

The elegantly curved angles of General Mica's Nouveau-Deco Radiant Buffet cabinet are made with post-formed lamination, a process which General Mica pioneered and which has become very popular on furniture. The caps and edging are available in chrome, brass, or silver. Constructed in lengths ranging from 78″ to 96″, the cabinet is 29″ high and 20″ deep and comes in models with two or four doors.

For further information, contact:

General Mica Corp.
1850 N.E. 144th St.
North Miami, FL 33181
(305) 949-7247

MODULAR MAPLE CHEST

Back in 1934, Gilbert Rohde was designing slightly rounded, knobless furniture in the Depression Modern style that was considered advanced for its time. Now that style has reemerged as postmodernists ransack the past for elements of design that can speak directly to the 1980s. Here Mondrian updates the 1930s in a stylish maple chest that reinterprets Depression modernism by accentuating horizontality. Available in twelve different sizes, the chest is well-suited to both office and residential use. Gilbert Rohde would have loved it.

For further information, contact:

Mondrian, Inc.
1021 Second Avenue
New York, NY 10022
(212) 355-7373

John McNanie

Si Chi Ko

ARMOIRE

Craftsmen have been creating armoires for hundreds of years. These massive pieces are, in effect, portable closets of great utility. There has never been an armoire quite like Rick Wrigley's. It is traditional in its form, but entirely contemporary in expression and substance. The entire piece is constructed of Colorcore, a moldable laminate by Formica. The pillars, arches, and frieze (painted by John Dowd) reflect Wrigley's fascination with postmodern decoration. So, too, do the humorous chipped and flaking painted patches and the illusionary bricks at the base. The bricks are actually drawers, and the doors to the armoire open to reveal a cedar-lined closet. The armoire measures 96" tall, 50" wide, and 30" deep.

For more information about his work, contact:

Rick Wrigley
80 Race St.
Holyoke, MA 01040
(413) 536-2034

BUTTERFLY CABINET AND SILVER CHEST

Cabinetmaker Anthony Giachetti achieves an unusual effect with his form-bent lamination (the process of creating curved wood with thin glued layers). His Butterfly cabinet manages to retain a rational form even as its doors and sides fan out wildly. The French walnut doors are made up of individual curved and fluted slats, assembled with tongue-and-groove and dovetailed joinery. The doors swing open from the center like wings on a butterfly, hence the cabinet's name. The cabinet case is made of black walnut and measures 66" by 31" by 19".

Made of East Indian rosewood and Honduras rosewood, Giachetti's silver chest and stand display the grace achieved with the technique of form-bent lamination. The entire piece measures 46" high, 32" wide, and 15" deep. The chest is lined with pacific cloth.

For further information about Giachetti's designs, contact:

Anthony Giachetti
Box 504
East Boothbay, ME 04544
(207) 633-3740

SPACE BUILDER AND ELFA BASKET SYSTEM

The Pottery Barn offers a number of sensible systems for storage. Its lightweight Space Builder can double the usable volume in a closet. 12″- and 16″-deep shelves accommodate a variety of objects from shoes to blankets. Their down-turned lips provide coat hanger space as well. (Hanging garments on several levels as shown here saves enormous amounts of room.) The Pottery Barn offers an assortment of anchoring clips, shelf brackets, end brackets, and shoe supports for sturdy installation.

The Swedish Elfa basket system, developed thirty years ago, is still an excellent solution to the dilemma of small spaces and large storage needs. Three sizes of baskets are available in a number of combinations. Casters and a rock maple butcher block cap make the system superior to most others. The entire assembly comes in two sizes—29″ or 41″ high, 18″ wide, and 21″ deep. The baskets come in depths of 3½″, 7½″, and 11½″. Made of steel, the baskets and frame have a bonded epoxy finish.

For the location of the Pottery Barn outlet nearest you, contact:

The Pottery Barn
175 Clearbrook Rd.
Elmsford, NY 10523
(914) 592-2330

CHEST

"I am currently concentrating on building gallery showpieces," says craftsman Ian Forsberg. "With these pieces I am able to push away from the constraints of fulfilling a specific function and concentrate instead on the visual and spatial impact." Fortunately, Forsberg also does commissioned work, and so it is possible to have this impressive chest or another like it in your home. The tambour doors are shown open to reveal the two drawers. Forsberg combines maple, Amazon yellowwood, and purpleheart to make the chest, and finishes it with a clear lacquer. It measures 13" high, 18" wide, and 20" deep.

For further information about Forsberg's work, contact:

Ian Forsberg
2042 Vine St.
Berkeley, CA 94709
(415) 548-4032

PLEXIGLASS MAGAZINE RACK

Relegate your magazines to a pile in a box, and it is a plain fact that you will never leaf through them again. On the other hand, if you keep them on a rack such as the one shown here from Plexi-Craft, not only will you rescue them from oblivion, but you will probably save them from dilapidation as well. The angled racks keep the magazines neatly stacked and uncreased. Made of ½"-thick clear plexiglass sides, the rack has ¼"-thick shelves. It measures 14" long, 10" deep, and 42½" high.

Catalogue, $2.

Plexi-Craft Quality Products Corp.
514 W. 24th St.
New York, NY 10011
(212) 924-3244

HAARLEM II SIDEBOARD

Ronald Carter, designer of the Haarlem II furniture series and many other collections for Peter Miles Furniture, is in the vanguard of European designers. He is one of only 70 Englishmen awarded the title RDI— Royal Designer for Industry. The sideboard illustrated here, imported by Interna Designs, testifies to Carter's imagination and skill. The construction is of solid hardwood—in this case, ash—with a veneered top, panels, inserts, and doors. The interior contains four adjustable shelves. Measurements are 3' 4" high by 5½' long by 1' 9" deep.

For further information, contact:

Interna Designs, Ltd.
The Merchandise Mart
Space 6-168
Chicago, IL 60654
(312) 467-6076

"EUROFORM" DIVISION BOOKCASES

These metal frame bookcases afford a great deal of flexibility because of their light structure. Far less monumental than wooden box-shaped shelves, Origlia's bookcases feature rounded melamine shelves and wicket-shaped frames. The frames are available in white, gray, black, yellow, red, blue, pink, or green; the shelves, in white or black. The entire assembly stands 43⅓", 55", 67", or 78⅔" high for the three-, four-, five-, and six-shelf models respectively. Bookends, coordinated in both shape and color to the frames, are also available.

For more information, contact:

Origlia USA Inc.
200 Lexington Ave.
New York, NY 10016
(212) 532-0075

GRAFFITI

Consolidation is the key to efficiency in storage. Graffiti reduces the enormous sizes of cabinets, bookcases, and desks into one integrated system. Made by Bieffe, it consists of steel components that can be assembled to fit individual needs. Graffiti includes uprights, various shelves that can serve as desk tops, rails, and an assortment of hooks. The mesh panel shown here can be used for hanging items. Graffiti comes in seven colors of epoxy coating.

For further information, contact:

**Gullan Henley International
227 W. 17th St.
New York, NY 10011
(212) 741-3384**

Other Suppliers of Furniture

Consult List of Suppliers for addresses.

Sofas, Settees, Love Seats, and Benches

Ambiant
Arconas Corporation
Avento
Brown Jordan Co.
Brueton Industries Inc.
Castelli Furniture Inc.
CI Designs
Cyrna International
Davis Furniture Industries, Inc.
Directional Furniture Showrooms
The Door Store
Dux
Erwin-Lambeth Inc.
Falcon Products Inc.
The Gunlocke Co., Inc.
Henredon Furniture Industries Inc.
ICF
IKEA
Jensen-Lewis Co. Inc.
Knoll International
Krug Inc.
Lübke
Cy Mann Designs
John Marcoux
Herman Miller, Inc.
Palazzetti, Inc.
Peter Pepper Products, Inc.
Plexability
Scalia Inc.
Scope Furniture Ltd.
Sunar
Tom Wessells
Workbench Contract

Tables

Abbacus Plastics
Ambiant
Arconas Corporation
Artemide Inc.
Atelier International Ltd.
Bieffe USA
J. & D. Brauner
Brayton International
Jon Brooks
Brueton Industries Inc.
Casa Bella Imports
The Children's Room
CI Designs

Michael Coffey
Davis Furniture Industries, Inc.
Domus International
The Door Store
Dux
David Ebner
Ello Furniture
Furniture of the Twentieth Century
Greenbaum Furniture
Gullan Henley International
H & Z Marbleworks, Inc.
Henredon Furniture Industries Inc.
IKEA
Intrends—Walker and Zanger
Jensen-Lewis Co. Inc.
Vladimir Kagan Designs
Kinetics
LaLune Willow Collection
Lübke
Cy Mann Designs
MDI Designs
Mondrian Furniture
Moser Contract Furniture
Peter Pepper Products, Inc.
Plexi-Craft Quality Products Corp.
The Pottery Barn
Powell & Tierney Furniture
Puccio Marble
Quatrelle, Inc.
Scalia Inc.
Scope Furniture Ltd.
Stendig International
Sunar
Western Arts & Tables
Workbench Contract
The Yellow Door

Beds

Avery Boardman-Headbed
Brown Jordan Co.
Dux
Ello Furniture
Greenbaum Furniture
Henredon Furniture Industries Inc.
IKEA
Jensen-Lewis Co. Inc.
Vladimir Kagan Designs
Mondrian Furniture
Murphy Door Bed Co.
Thayer Coggin
Wall • Goldfinger Design Associates
Tom Wessells

Chairs

Abacus Plastics
Ambiant
Artemide
Atelier International

Bieffe USA
J.B. Blunk
J. & D. Brauner
Brayton International
Jon Brooks
Brueton Industries Inc.
Casa Bella Imports
Castelli Furniture
The Children's Room
Cy Mann Designs
Michael Coffey
Davis Furniture Industries, Inc.
The Door Store
Dunbar
Dux
David Ebner
Furniture of the Twentieth Century
General Mica Corporation
Gotemobler
Gullan Henley International
The Gunlocke Co.
Haworth Inc.
Heinz & Co.
Henredon Furniture Industries Inc.
ICF Inc.
IKEA
Intrends International
Dakota Jackson
Jensen-Lewis Co., Inc.
Kafra Modern
Vladimir Kagan Designs
John Kapel
Kinetics
Krug Inc.
LaLune Willow Collection
The Albert Martin Company
MDI—Meuble Design Inc.
Herman Miller, Inc.
Nemschoff Chairs Inc.
Nienkämper
Origlia
The Pace Collection
Plexi-Craft Quality Products Corp.
Powell & Tierney Furniture
Scandiline
Scope Furniture Ltd.
Sunar
Tec Designs
Thonet Industries
Bob Trotman
Wall • Goldfinger
Westnofa USA, Inc.
Workbench Contract

Desks

Abacus Plastics
Atelier International
Bieffe USA
Brayton International

Brueton Industries Inc.
The Children's Room
Davis Furniture Industries, Inc.
The Door Store
Greenbaum Furniture
Gullan Henley International
Haworth Inc.
Henredon Furniture Industries Inc.
IKEA
Interna Designs, Ltd.
Kinetics
Knoll International
Lübke
Mondrian, Inc.
The Pace Collection
Plexability
Karl Springer Ltd.
Stendig International
Sunar Ltd.
Wall • Goldfinger Design Associates
Workbench Contract

Storage and Shelving

Abacus Plastics
Arthemis Inc.
Atelier International
Avanti Furniture Corp.
Brueton Industries Inc.
The Children's Room
Classic Moulders
Cy Mann Designs
Davis & Warshow Inc.
Directional Furniture Showrooms
The Door Store
Dux
Ello Furniture Manufacturing Co.
Erwin-Lambeth Inc.
Gia International Designs, Inc.
P.E. Guerin Inc.
The Gunlocke Co.
ICF
IKEA
Jensen-Lewis Co., Inc.
Vladimir Kagan Designs Inc.
Knoll International
Luxurious Laminates
Modern Mode
The Pace Collection
Poggenpohl
Quatrelle, Inc.
Roche-Bobois
St. Charles Manufacturing Co.
Saporiti Italia
Scalia
Scandinavia Design Inc.
Sunar Ltd.
Workbench Contract

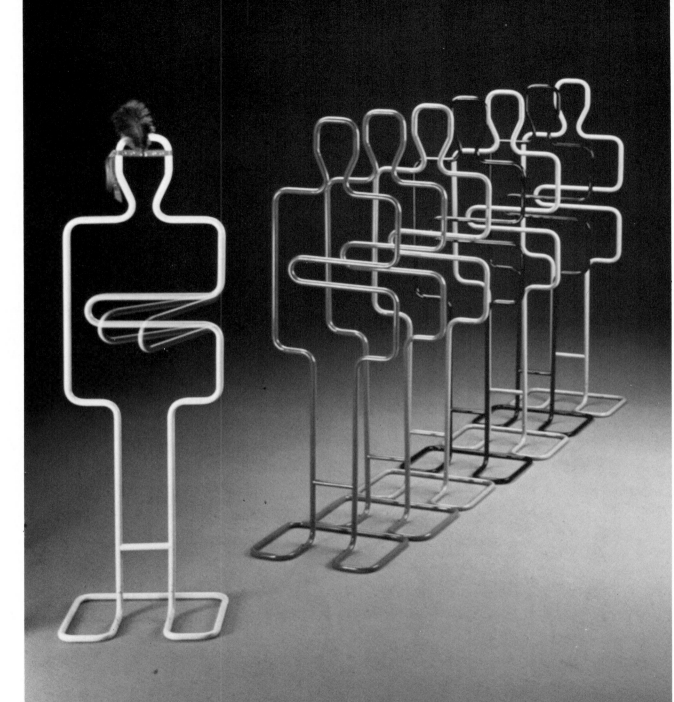

6.

Decorative Accessories

Even after plugging in the lights, covering the walls and floor, and moving in the furniture, you have not yet finished decorating a room. The little things are still missing. Without accessories, a room can end up being barren and coldly inhuman, and, if they are selected carelessly, the dissonance of opposing details can destroy the overall design. The sleek look of a contemporary desk will not be helped by the presence of a marmalade jar serving as a pencil holder.

The objects shown in this chapter are quite varied—the reader can find clocks, desk accessories, dinnerware, vases, wall hangings, and many other products. Some of these items, like salt and pepper shakers, are plain necessities which often go unnoticed but can be given life under the hand of an imaginative craftsman. Other more unusual accessories do not spring immediately to a consumer's mind when trying to outfit a room. A decorative bell or a tapestry may seem frivolous and impractical, but its unconventional look may actually crown a design.

The majority of accessories that follow come from craftsmen who carefully construct them by hand, using very personal techniques. Of consequence, they have an intimacy about them, almost a friendship with their owners. The attractiveness of major elements of design comes from the way in which they form an overall composition in a room, like the objects in a painting. Accessories, on the other hand, because of their much smaller scale, generally have a compact, hand-held type of beauty that offers a more personal delight.

Servetto coat hanger from Origlia USA, Inc.

GOOD HEAVENS!

Telling time by the stars has never been this easy. Steve Diskin designed this time piece for Kovacs Design Group, which offers a large range of inventive clocks. Diskin's has an outer ring with a white dot to indicate the minute, a recessed ring with a large dark disk to indicate the hour, and finally a recessed disk in the center to indicate the second. The entire assembly is 11″ in diameter and 2½″ deep. It is quartz-accurate and uses C batteries.

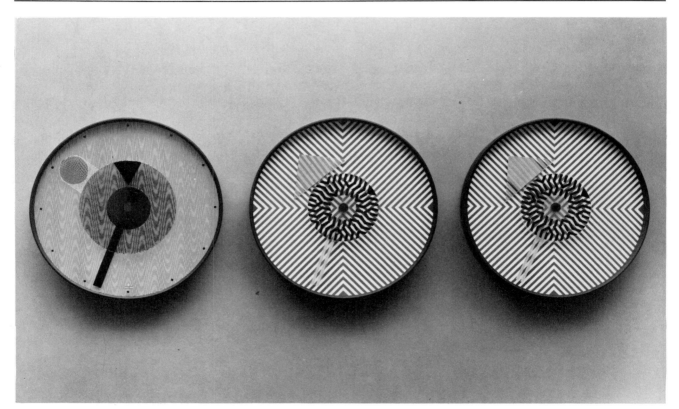

KINETIC 1 AND KINETIC 2

Certain to catch your attention, even when you don't want the time, the Kinetic 1 and Kinetic 2 clocks are energetic combinations of colors and lines. Designed by Barbara Kovacs, the Kinetic 1 (pictured at the left) has a disk of bold waves at the center of its face, as well as black and white hands and dial pattern.

The Kinetic 2 has a gray and white pattern and either gray and red or pink and green hands. The quartz movement of these clocks is powered by a C battery, and the clock face is bordered by a matte-black steel rim 11″ in diameter and 2½″ deep.

George Post

TUBE DESK CLOCK

Designed by Alan Peckolick and offered by Kovacs Design Group, this original clock is not only a straightforward indicator of time but also a handsome element on a desk top. The horizontally rotating face has a battery-powered quartz movement. The fixture itself is solid brass, 10″ high and 4½″ in diameter, and is available in matte black, gloss white, or polished brass.

Catalogue available.

Kovacs Design Group Inc.
330 E. 59th St.
New York, NY 10022
(212) 838-3400

INLAID CLOCK

Over the span of ten years of work and experimentation, Robert McKeown has developed a method of cloisonné in wood that is uncommonly personal. McKeown describes the painstaking process as a combination of inlay and resin cast around wood inserts. Each section of colored resin

must dry before the next can be started, and so one piece takes days to construct. The assembly of his products also requires careful attention to the cutting and exact fitting of wood. The attention to detail that all of this work demands reveals itself in the beautiful pieces that McKeown offers to the public—a wide range of boxes, desk accessories, and clocks such as the modern version of a Mission-style

clock shown here, featuring exotic woods and a battery-operated quartz movement.

Catalogue available.

Robert McKeown
23970 Azevedo Ave.
Haywood, CA 94541
(415) 582-4914

KALEIDOSCOPE CLOCK

Irving Harper demonstrates with his "new wave" kaleidoscope clock, designed for Howard Miller, that the new is often simply the rejuvenated old. With all the colors of an earlier psychedelic age, Harper's clock displays the hour marks without numbers. The minute hand is a thin white marker and the hour hand a white circle. In addition, the second hand is not a hand at all, but a pinwheel of reds and blues spinning on the inner disk. This clock, featuring an injection-molded case, an acrylic lens, and quartz battery movement, is 9″ in diameter and 3″ in depth.

For further information, contact:

Howard Miller Clock Company
860 East Main Street
Zeeland, MI 49464
(616) 772-9131

PETER PEPPER CLOCKS

The clocks by Peter Pepper Products are not your normal, dull business clocks. While intended for use in banks, offices, hospitals, and the like, these clocks have arresting designs. In this case, though, aesthetics complement practicality: the very boldness of their appearance makes them readable as far away as 200 feet. The clock illustrated here (#394), for example, has a black and white face and polished red hands and border. It is

12″ in diameter, with an acrylic face and 1¾″ of steel housing. It is equipped with a quartz crystal movement. Peter Pepper Products offers a large range of clocks besides this one, both with hands or with digital readout.

For further information, contact:

Peter Pepper Products, Inc.
17929 S. Susana Road
Compton, CA 90224
(213) 979-0815

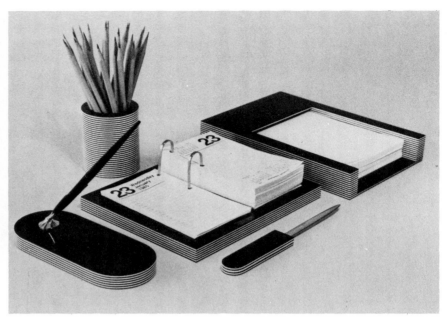

DESK ACCESSORIES

Bailey & Company of Los Angeles has come up with a singular way to manage the clutter on one's desk. The pen dispenser, pencil holder, pad holder, calendar, and letter opener illustrated here are all color-coordinated, composed of thin layers of surfacing materials. Bailey's desk accessories come in an extraordinary array of 94 colors.

For more information, contact:

Bailey & Company
P.O. Box 8366
Calabasas, CA 91302
(714) 672-2470

MOMA DESK ACCESSORIES

These coordinated accessories from Italy are well suited to the dark, sleek styles of contemporary home or office desks. The pearwood "vaschetti" (box) shown here is designed by G. Pizzitutti and manufactured by GIPI.

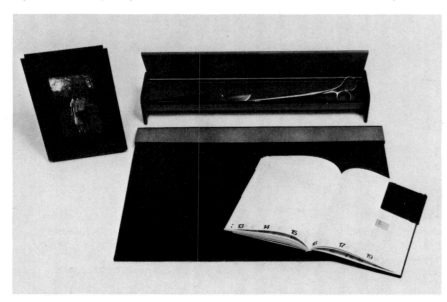

Soft tones of pearwood combine with black rubber trim on the outside, and on the inside is a rubber grid floor in a curved depression. The 20″ length, 4¾″ width, and 2¾″ height make the box an excellent storage container for necessities such as letter openers and scissors. The accompanying canvas blotter, designed by Marco Baldini and manufactured by Edizioni & C. Firenze, features a calf leather border at the top that can clamp paper in place. The blotter measures 21½″ by 15¼″. The photo frame shown here is designed and manufactured by the makers of the blotter. The black canvas frame measures 8″ by 6½″ and has an acetate sleeve. Finally, an "Impatto 7" appointment book, designed by H. Waibl and made by Nava Milano, comes with these accessories. Printed in five languages, the book features one-week, double-page spreads for two years' worth of planning and is bound in a 7″ by 9″ black cover.

For more information, contact:

Dakota Jackson
306 E. 61st St.
New York, NY 10021
(212) 838-9444

Another set of desk accessories offered by the Museum of Modern Art, this group is characterized by an economy of style. The tape dispenser, for example, designed and manufactured in Denmark by Strategi/Holmbäck ApS, consists of a simple block of aluminum, carved by a computerized lathe. It measures 2¾" by 4⅛" by 1¾". The heliocoidal letter opener is one piece of satin-finished stainless steel curved gently for handling. Designed by Enzo Mari and made in Italy by Danese, it measures ½" by ¾" by 8⅜". The address book is designed and produced by Marco Baldini; it is thumb-indexed, has a 100% cotton canvas cover, and has dimensions of 9½" by 6½" by ½". A "twin" pen which also comes with the set, offers a tungsten ball point pen tip or a .5 mm lead pencil tip, depending on the direction one turns the pen barrel. The brushed stainless-steel pen (with a black titanium-oxide finish) is designed by Gerd Muller and produced by Lamy in Germany. "Ritronic 2" is a portfolio designed by Norbert Link and Sutsass Associati and made by Nava Milano in Italy. Graph and lined paper are housed in the gray leather portfolio, along with a solar-powered calculator. Opened, it measures 23" by 13½".

Catalogue, $2.

Mail Order Department
Museum of Modern Art
11 W. 53rd St.
New York, NY 10019
(212) 708-9888

DINNERWARE

"We have been influenced," explain Sandra and Richard Farrell, "by the long tradition of Oriental ceramics and by the attitudes of abstract expressionism in early modern painting. Water, light, color, feeling, and the essence of landscape are continual sources of inspiration. Our works of both architectural and functional porcelain are intended to communicate images and emotions through the movement of color and the play of light on their glassy surfaces." The Farrells create these movements of colors with an ancient technique of coating their pieces with several differently colored layers of glaze and firing them at very high temperatures. The colors interact to form sweeping combinations of new tints. In addition to such handsome dinnerware as the set shown, the Farrells make colorful tiles for wall decorations.

For further information, contact:

Farrell Porcelain
P.O. Box 108
East Killingly, CT 06243
(203) 774-8967

ARC MIRRORS

Dakota Jackson makes all types of furniture and accessories, and considers meticulous craftsmanship for each object to be of primary importance. His Arc mirror, for example, consists of scored and brushed uprights with wood detailing and marble caps. The arc over the mirror is available in either a wood or lacquered finish. The entire assembly measures 40" by 60", and the mirror itself is ¼"-thick clear glass.

DECANTER SET

Wayne Filan, educated at both the
Philadelphia College of Art and the
Royal College of Art in London,
reflects his sophisticated approach to
glassware with every piece he makes.
His works have been exhibited extensively in the U.S., as well as in
England and Ireland. The decanter
set shown here is an example of
Filan's cultivated technique. The
handblown black glass is curved with
restraint and contrasts magnificently
with the tadpole-like decorations of
platinum plate on each piece. The
decanter measures 12″ high.

For further information, contact:

Wayne Filan
Shoreham, VT 05770
(802) 897-2606

Erik Borg

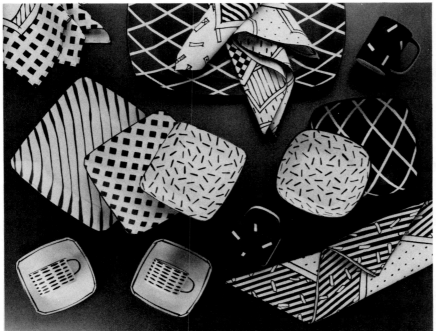

S. Baker Vail

STATS DINNER SERVICE

Dorothy Hafner has designed
porcelain and textiles for several
highly prestigious firms, including
Neimann Marcus, Tiffany & Co., and
West Germany's Rosenthal Studio.
(Hafner is the first American woman to
work for the German firm.) Hafner
also creates works on commission for
individuals. Stats, shown here, is a
series of porcelain bowls, platters,
cups, and even vases, with coordinated napkins, all designed with her
characteristically energetic handling
of stripes and spots.

For more information, contact:

Dorothy Hafner
44 Cooper Square #3R
New York, NY 10003
(212) 677-9797

GLASS BOWLS AND FLASKS

Flowing white arms of glass embrace curving black bowls to summon up the sensuous feeling of these Paul Hanson works. Their heights range from 5″ to 8½″, and the middle bowl shown here reaches 19″ across.

Hanson's sharply geometrical vases come in a variety of smoke grays, reds, and blues. They stand between 8″ and 11″ high and are made of satin glass.

For further information about these pieces and other handcrafted bowls, flasks, and vases, contact:

Paul Hanson
610 Commercial Avenue
Carlstadt, NJ 07072
(201) 933-4873

WRIGHT DINNERWARE

After Frank Lloyd Wright designed the Imperial Hotel in Tokyo in 1922, he designed dinnerware for its dining room. Noritake, the world's largest porcelain manufacturer, made the set until the building was demolished in 1968. The Imperial Hotel Company has granted Heinz & Co., a maker of Wright reproductions, permission to sell a limited series of the dinnerware. The set consists of a salad bowl and plate, a dinner plate, bread plate, soup bowl, and cup and saucer. The logo is a red circle surrounded by a pale yellow ring and orbiting pastel-colored disks. The style is ingeniously at once Japanese and Western.

For more information, contact:

Heinz & Co.
P.O. Box 663
Oak Park, IL 60303
(312) 383-1310

Susie Cushner

JOINED DINNERWARE

Robin Mix creates the Joined series of glass platters and bowls by spinning them into desired shapes in front of a fired kiln. The results are attractive pieces with exotic colors—orange and purple, blue and black, or red and celadon. The platter shown here measures 16″ in diameter; the bowl is 9½″ wide and 5″ high.

For further information, contact:

Robin Mix
Tunbridge Glassworks
Tunbridge, VT 05077
(802) 889-3430

PEWTER SHAKERS

Jon Route has an intimate relationship with the metals with which he works. "It satisfies a desire of mine to completely control or dominate something. I can make the metal do whatever I damn well please." It pleased Route to create the pewter salt, sugar, and pepper shakers shown here. Standing

4″ high, the 3″-wide shakers fit together to form a cylinder. They are made from 16-gauge pewter and have file and satin finishes.

For further information, contact:

Jon Route
P.O. Box 4823
Overland Park, KS 66204
(913) 648-6099

ART DECO PIECES

Hap Sakwa's lively and colorful Art Deco creations, ranging from candy dishes to lamps, generally feature bold layers and tiers.

The abstract painter Kandinsky lends little more than his name to the Kandinsky candy dish shown here. The dish is made of turned wood with acrylic lacquer in red on the rings and black on the body. It measures 9½″ tall and 8½″ wide.

The three-legged fruit bowl named "Mrs. Moore," features turned wood as well, with acrylic lacquer. The black legs, capped with red spheres, stand 7″ tall and support a gold-colored 15″-wide bowl with ample room for fruit for Mrs. Moore—or anyone else for that matter.

For further information, contact:

Hap Sakwa
1330 8th St.
Baywood Park, CA 93402
(805) 528-7585

GLAZED DINNERWARE

Judith Weber likes to accommodate her customers: she is eager to meet the needs of designers, shop owners, or retail customers, creating dinnerware suited for their home interiors. She offers an extensive color search at her studio from her file of colors, to be sure that the customer is satisfied. She will even create new colors as the need arises for individual tastes. Weber gives a sensuous touch to both her pottery and her glazing. The four-

his Gourd series, made of Emery oak. Rings radiate from a beautiful central imperfection in the wood to create a sophisticated (and yet natural) design on this 8″-tall, 9″-wide piece.

For further information, contact:

Todd Hoyer
139 Higgins Hill
P.O. Box 1451
Bisbee, AZ 85603
(602) 432-4893

PORCELAIN VASES

Robert Levine's medium of choice for pottery is porcelain, and his vessels consequently have a crystalline-like appearance and a high sheen. Levine experiments with the various aspects of glazed porcelain and often incorporates several such characteristics in one work. The vase shown here is a good example of this approach: blue specks streak a field of tin-colored glaze. In some ways, this 20″ by 20″ urn has an organic quality to it that much modern pottery tries to create, as the blue seems to grow like lichen over the vessel. Nonetheless, Levine preserves a classic form for his work by the proportions he chooses. Levine's vessels can place an accent on the style of a room that few other objects can, although the room's decor must be quite strong to blend with the striking look of this craftsman's works.

piece setting shown here features a rich triangular pattern of glazing in glossy gray and stoney gray-black. The dinner plate measures 11½″ in diameter; the luncheon plate, 8″; and the soup bowl, 6″. The cup has a nine-ounce capacity.

The handle on Weber's teapot is the central element in its graceful curving design. Colored with a stone-black matte, it has a six-cup capacity.

For further information, contact:

Judith Weber
50 Webster Ave.
New Rochelle, NY 10801
(914) 235-9027

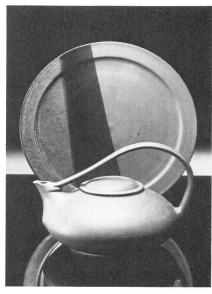

WOODEN VASES

Most woodworking extracts natural irregularities from wood—knots, burls, and so on. In doing so, craftsmen can neglect a major dimension of wood design in favor of straight, inoffensive grains. Todd Hoyer respects the design a tree creates for itself and allows it free rein. He lathes pieces of wood into vases and sculptures, such as the one shown here, a vase from

Richard Byrd

Robert Levine pieces can be purchased through:

**The Works Gallery East
28A Jobs Lane
Southampton, NY 11968
(516) 283-5093**

**The Levine/Davis Studio
1601 Guilford
Baltimore, Maryland 21202
(301) 659-0978**

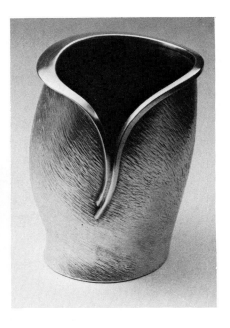

For more information, contact:

**Jon Route
P.O. Box 4823
Overland Park, KS 66204
(913) 648-6099**

Susie Cushner

TRIAD

By avoiding the simple method of blowing and then shaping a glass bubble, Robin Mix gives his triangular vessels a luxurious unconventionality. As exotic as it appears, Triad serves as a practical pitcher or vase. It is made of colored opaque glass with a contrasting thread of glass on the rim. Six color combinations are available— yellow and green, gray-blue and red, chartreuse and green, sea green and orange, lavender and green, and white and black.

For further information, contact:

**Robin Mix
Tunbridge Glassworks
Tunbridge, VT 05077
(802) 889-3430**

LIP VASE

Jon Route's designs in pewter, gold, and silver are lyrically modern, and yet Route says himself, "I love the feel of a good hammer, the look of an anvil, and the smell of coal burning on a hot forge." From Route's hot forge emerges the pewter vase shown here. Measuring 4″ by 3″ by 3″, both the satin-finished forged lip and the file-finished body are formed out of 16-gauge pewter.

ARRAS TAPESTRIES

There is very little in the way of weaving that Arras Tapestries will not do for you. Bella Zwicker, together with a staff of ten, offers a range of hangings and area rugs. If you find a tapestry they have designed that you like so much that you want one wider than the usual six feet, Arras is willing to oblige. On the other hand, if you have a design of your own in mind, the firm will make you a custom tapestry. Prices for custom work depend on the design and dimensions requested. Bella Zwicker also offers limited editions of her own works, each series consisting of 100 copies.

Illustrated here is *Dunes*, a 60″ by 74″ hanging in various earth tones. The characteristic waves of color found here and on many other Arras works complement interior designs of contemporary homes and offices. (Among the commissions Arras Tapestries has received is a custom tapestry for the Sahara Hotel in Las Vegas.)

For further information, contact:

Arras Tapestries
203 E. Broadway
Suite 207
Glendale, CA 91205
(213) 244-7297

ZIGZAG TAPESTRY

Trained in design, dyeing, and Japanese Ikat, Mary Colton makes woven garments and wall hangings

that are fusions of her diverse learning. She specializes in warp and weft Ikats and painted warp pieces. "Zigzag" is one of her creations, an interlocking tapestry in black and white. Measuring 60″ by 30″ by ¼″, the tapestry is made of wool with a linen warp.

For further information, contact:

Mary Rawcliffe Colton
2821 Indiana N.E.
Albuquerque, NM 87110
(505) 881-3944

WALL HANGING AND QUILTS

The relationship of colors—the ways in which they blend or contrast—preoccupies the work of David Cress, a maker of tapestries, tufted rugs, and quilts. C.S.C.R., named for its constituent materials—cotton, silk, chenille,

and raffia—mixes white, blues, greens, and oranges with a soft maroon background. The tapestry measures 40″ by 56″. Also shown is Cress's quilt, Burning Bush, which derives an intense central heat by combining horizontal and vertical strips of cotton in various combinations of colors. It measures 84″ by 118″.

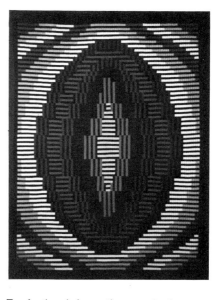

For further information, contact:

David Cress
274 N. Goodman St.
Rochester, NY 14607
(716) 442-9657

Cress's work is also available through:

Rosanne Raab Associates
60 Franklin Road
Scarsdale, NY 10583
(914) 472-8788

IMAGES OF JAPAN—STUDY #2

This tapestry gains its singular style from Ruth Gowell's use of the warp face method of weaving and from unusual selections of materials for the

200

weft. "Images of Japan" has electrical cord and monofilament for its weft and rayon for the warp. Measuring 30″ high, 32″ wide, and 2″ thick, the tapestry is shown here with an aluminum section frame.

For further information, contact:

Ruth Gowell
7010 Aronow Dr.
Falls Church, VA 22042
(703) 532-8645

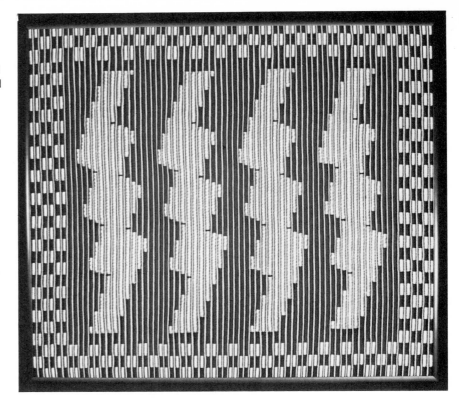

EMBOSSED PAPER DESIGNS

Marjorie Tomchuk makes both embossings in color and cast-paper art such as the piece illustrated here. Her handmade paper is approximately ¼″ thick and thus provides a sensuous tone to all her works. The subjects of her pieces are quite varied—wheatfield landscapes, galactic panoramas, ocean scenes, and moments of sunlight. For each subject, she uses stunningly appropriate colors. Tomchuk recently has expanded her projects at times into diptychs, triptychs, and quartets. In addition, she has made limited editions of posters for art expositions in Washington, California, New York, and Texas.

Color catalogues of Marjorie Tomchuk's work are available for $3 each. Brochures are also available at no cost.

Marjorie Tomchuk
44 Horton Lane
New Canaan, CT 06840
(203) 972-0137

John L. Manning

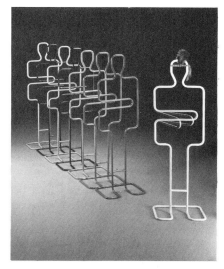

BONE AND WOOD DESIGNS

Aged bone makes for beautiful creations, such as Robert Chadwick's stylish box shown here. Dovetailed and inlaid with ebony, the box has an attractively contrasting design. Chadwick's boxes vary from 3″ square in size to 6″ by 10″, and each is coated with a special combination of oils and finishes. The craftsman also builds other products out of bone, such as chopsticks and desk accessories, and works occasionally with precious woods.

For further information, contact:

Robert Chadwick
325 Red Pump Rd.
Nottingham, PA 19362
(215) 932-8637

SERVETTO COAT HANGER

The clothes hanger has taken some very tortuous rearrangements from Origlia to create the Servetto. Iron tubes, ingeniously forming a human frame, permit the hanging of coats, shirts, or jackets, and a supple arm allows pants. Available in eight colors of epoxy finishes, the Servetto can complement the design of a bedroom, dressing room, or even entrance hallway. It comes in white, gray, black, yellow, green, red, pink, or blue.

For more information, contact:

Origlia USA, Inc.
200 Lexington Ave.
New York, NY 10016
(212) 532-0075

COAT HOOKS AND RACKS

Whether you are passionately determined to design your house in a modern style right down to the coat hooks, or you just need a place to hang your jacket, Curvalinear is worth your attention. The coat hooks and coat rack shown here are made of red oak finished in a light stain and three coats of low gloss lacquer. They come with brass anchoring equipment as well. The large coat hooks measure 8½″ high, 1⅛″ wide, and 2½″ deep. The smaller hooks measure 4⅝″ high, 1⅛″ wide, and 2½″ deep. The coat rack, with five hooks, measures 5″ high, 26⅞″ wide, and 2⅞″ deep.

For further information, contact:

Curvalinear
115 14th Ave. S.
Seattle, WA 98144
(206) 323-5471

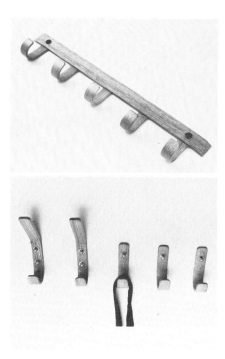

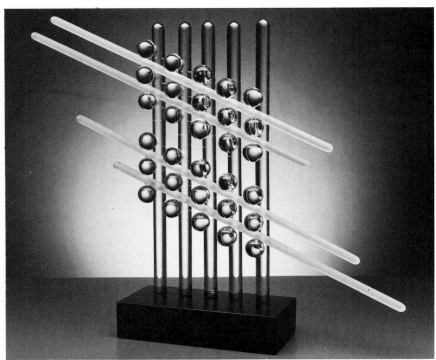

BELLS, BELLS, BELLS

Robert Fisher of U.S. Bells makes
bells which mix the beauty of sound
with that of appearance; the serenely
beautiful and well-designed structure
visually echoes its knell. Fisher makes
a variety of bells, ranging from the
doorbell shown here, to dinner bells,
to his extraordinary wind bells that are
unquestionably pieces of sculpture.
Fisher says that his present goal is to
cast a perfect Japanese temple bell—
but in the meantime he will continue
to make his attractive brass and
bronze tintinnabulators.

For more information, contact:

U.S. Bells/Richard Fisher
Prospect Harbor, ME 04469
(207) 963-7184

GLASS SCULPTURE

The glass sculptures of Hans Godo
Fräbel are available only at his gallery
in Atlanta, where several artisans and
apprentices assist him. "Flash,"
shown here, features crystal rods and
spheres along with sandblasted
diagonal rods. The sculpture
measures 24″ high and 26″ wide, and
the base is 6″ deep.

For further information about Fräbel's
works, contact:

The Fräbel Gallery
231 Peachtree St. N.E.
Atlanta, GA 30303
(404) 659-2832

WOOD CLOISONNÉ

Robert McKeown's jewelry box, "Red
Pyramid," bears witness to his artistic
individuality and excellence. McKeown
has perfected a unique method of

wood cloisonné over the years, consisting of inlay and resin cast around
wood inserts. The lid of "Red
Pyramid" has inlaid ebony and ivory

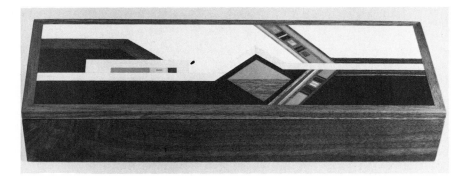

with accents of orange, blue, and gold. Measuring 11¾″ by 4½″ by 2″, the box is made of maple and black walnut.

Catalogue available.

Robert McKeown
23970 Azevedo Ave.
Haywood, CA 94541
(415) 582-4914

MORE MOMA DESIGNS

The Museum of Modern Art offers everything from pencil sharpeners to classic furniture reproductions in its Museum store. The two decorative accessories presented here are just a sampling of its extraordinary inventory.

The fashionable design and large capacities of today's telephone are both found in the Alpha X Telephone. Designed by René Moutet and made by Générale Electronique Européene in France, the phone features a

microprocessor memory. With it, a user can store 255 numbers which can be recalled by typing the name of the party being telephoned. A lock preserves the privacy of the memory, and a battery maintains it for up to a year in case of power failure or traveling. The phone also comes with a luminous display, a hold button, and amplifier, and a carrying case. It weighs 3½ pounds and measures 10½″ by 9″ by 3½″.

Alvar Aalto designed this umbrella stand in 1939, and today it still retains its contemporary style and practicality. The triangular brackets are made of bent plywood and attached to birch supports. A plastic basin fits into the base to collect the umbrella drippings.

For more information, contact:

Mail Order Department
Museum of Modern Art
11 W. 53rd St.
New York, NY 10019
(212) 708-9888

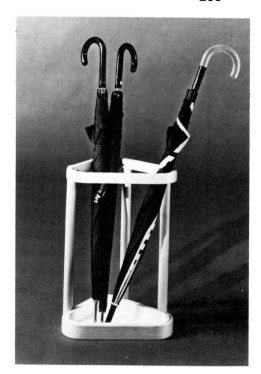

BUTTERFLY BOX

René Soulard, a woodworker from Seattle, finds time among his more prodigious projects with furniture- and house-building to make smaller, whimsical objects such as this butterfly-shaped case. Usable as a jewelry box, the 10″ by 14″ container has a compartment under each wing-section-shaped lid. Soulard also makes a jewelry case in the shape of a moth.

For more information, contact:

René Soulard
1833 13th Ave. #208
Seattle, WA 98122
(206) 328-1164

Other Suppliers of
Decorative Accessories

*Consult List of Suppliers for
addresses*

Ambience
AMS Imports
Atelier International, Ltd.
Barbara Barron and Al Granek
BPC Industries
Morgan Bockius Studios
Glenn Brill
Stanley Bulbach
Casa Bique Ltd.
Glassmasters Guild
Italia Imports
Bruce Lenore
Williams Lyons Design Craft, Inc.
Mark McDonnell
Jeanne Otis
Anne Flatin Pixley
The Pottery Barn
Smith Metal Arts Company Inc.
Janet Taylor
Seth Thomas
Workbench

List of Suppliers

Abacus Plastics
135 W. 26th St.
New York, NY 10001
(212) 947-8990

Abbaka
435 23rd St.
San Francisco, CA 94107
(415) 648-7210

AEG-Household Appliances
U.S. Importer: Andi-Co.
Suite 301
2100 North Central Rd.
Fort Lee, NJ 07024
(201) 585-9362

Algemene Fluweelweverij
Agent: V. Guttman Corp.
95 Madison Ave.
New York, NY 10016
(212) 689-1899

Allmilmo Corp.
P.O. Box 629
70 Clinton Rd.
Fairfield, NJ 07006
(201) 227-2502

Amaru Tile International
D & D Building
979 Third Ave.
New York, NY 10022
(212) 750-8804

Alpha Design Studio, Inc.
613 S. 21st Ave.
Hollywood, FL 33020
(305) 920-8999

Ambiant
The Merchandise Mart
Suite 861
Chicago, IL 60654
(312) 644-2111

Or in Canada:

76 Richmond St. East
Toronto, ONT M5C 1P1
Canada
(416) 863-0863

Ambience
979 Third Ave.
New York, NY 10022
(212) 688-0170

Amerec Corp.
P.O. Box 3825
Bellevue, WA 98009
(800) 426-0848

American Olean Tile Co.
1000 Cannon Ave.
Lansdale, PA 19446
(215) 855-1111

American Marble & Flooring Co.
2516 Third Ave. S.
Birmingham, AL 35233
(205) 328-0384

AMS Imports
23 Ash Lane
Amherst, MA 01002
(413) 253-2644

Andi-Co.
Suite 301
2100 North Central Rd.
Fort Lee, NJ 07024
(201) 585-9362

Diana Arcadipone
5 Goodwin Pl., #3
Boston, MA 02114
(617) 338-2173

Architectural Emphasis, Inc.
2743 9th St.
Berkeley, CA 94710
(415) 644-2737

Architectural Paneling, Inc.
979 Third Ave.
New York, NY 10022
(212) 371-9632

Architectural Pottery
3601 Aviation Blvd.
Manhattan Beach, CA 90266
(213) 643-9103

Arconas Corporation
580 Orwell St.
Mississauga, ONT L5A 3V7
Canada
(416) 272-0727

New York Showroom:

150 E. 58th St.
New York, NY 10022
(212) 753-4960

ARD Custom Kitchens & Baths
1 Fourth Pl.
Brooklyn, NY 11231
(718) 624-5688

Armstrong World Industries, Inc.
Box 3001
Lancaster, PA 17604
(717) 397-0611

Arras Tapestries
203 E. Broadway, Suite 207
Glendale, CA 91205
(818) 244-7297

Art Directions Inc.
6120 Delmar
St. Louis, MO 63112
(314) 863-1895

Artemide
150 E. 58th St.
New York, NY 10155
(212) 980-0710

Arthemis Inc.
17 N.E. 39th St.
Miami, FL 33137
(305) 573-3495

Artistic Brass
4100 Ardmore Ave.
South Gate, CA 90280
(213) 564-1100

Atag USA Corp.
2605 Broadway Ave.
Evanston, IL 60201
(312) 869-1900

Atelier International, Ltd.
595 Madison Ave.
New York, NY 10022
(212) 644-0400

Audio Designs Assoc.
602-610 Mamaroneck Ave.
White Plains, NY 10605
(914) 949-5926

Auger Designs Ltd.
979 Third Ave.
New York, NY 10022
(212) 486-1200

Avanti Furniture Corp.
497 Main St.
Farmingdale, NY 11735
(516) 293-8220

Avento
200 Lexington Ave.
New York, NY 10016
(212) 679-9114

Axiom Designs
110 Greene St.
New York, NY 10012
(212) 219-2212

Bailey & Company
P.O. Box 8366
Calabasas, CA 91302
(714) 672-2470

Marni Bakst Glass
235 E. 5th St., #2
New York, NY 10003
(212) 533-2556

Baldwin Hardware Corp.
841 Wyomissing Blvd., Box 82
Reading, PA 19603
(215) 777-7811

Baluchi Marble Ltd.
Pacific Design Center
8687 Melrose Ave., Suite 432
Los Angeles, CA 90069
(213) 659-3832

Charles Barone Inc.
9505 W. Jefferson Blvd.
Culver City, CA 90230
(213) 559-7211

Barbara Barron & Al Granek
1943 New York Ave.
Huntington Station, NY 11746
(516) 549-4242

Bath Interiors International
1903 Market
Denver, CO 80202
(303) 292-2100

Bendix Mouldings, Inc.
235 Pegasus Ave.
Northvale, NJ 07647
(201) 767-8888

Joel Berman Associates, Inc.
42-03 35th St.
Long Island City, NY 11101
(718) 729-2020

George Berry
745 Edgewood Ave. N.E.
Atlanta, GA 30307
(404) 577-4433

Beylerian
305 E. 63rd St.
New York, NY 10021
(212) 755-6300

Bieffe USA
U.S. Importer: GHI
227 W. 17th St.
New York, NY 10011
(212) 741-3384

Bigelow-Sanford Inc.
Box 3089
Greenville, SC 29602
(803) 299-2000

Norton Blumenthal
979 Third Ave.
New York, NY 10022
(212) 752-2535

J.B. Blunk
P.O. Box 83
Inverness, CA 94937
(415) 669-1458

Avery Boardman-Headbed
979 Third Ave.
New York, NY 10022
(212) 688-6611

Morgan Bockius Studios
1412 York Rd.
Warminster, PA 18974
(215) 672-6547

Boyd Lighting Co.
56 12th St.
San Francisco, CA 94103
(415) 431-4300

BPC Industries
Adams at Eleventh
Hoboken, NJ 07030
(201) 798-0100

J & D Brauner, Inc.
11-15 49th Ave.
Long Island City, NY 11101
(212) 392-1095

Brayton International Collection
255 Swathmore Ave.
P.O. Box 7288
High Point, NC 27264
(919) 434-4151

Glenn Brill
The Hand and the Spirit Crafts Gallery
4222 N. Marshall Way
Scottsdale, AZ 85251
(602) 946-4529

Jon Brooks
Pine Rd.
New Boston, NH 03070
(603) 487-2780

Brown Jordan Co.
9860 Gidley St.
P.O. Box 5688
El Monte, CA 91734
(818) 443-8971

Bruce Hardwood Floors
16803 Dallas Pkwy., Box 660100
Dallas, TX 75248
(214) 931-3000

Brueton Industries Inc.
227-02 145th Rd.
Springfield Gardens, NY 11413
(718) 527-3000

Brunschwig & Fils
979 Third Ave.
New York, NY 10022
(212) 838-7878

Bryan Plastics Ltd.
8451 Dalton Rd.
Town of Mount Royal
Quebec, H4T 1V5
Canada
(514) 733-5341

Stanley Bulbach
239 W. 15th St.
New York, NY 10011
(212) 243-9010

Calger
200 Lexington Ave., Suite 801
New York, NY 10016
(212) 689-9511

Caracalla Contemporary Baths Ltd.
969 Third Ave.
New York, NY 10022
(212) 753-9322

Carefree Wallcoverings, Collins & Aikman
Corp.
Chase Hill Rd.
Ashaway, RI 02804
(401) 377-2283

Carlton V
979 Third Ave.
New York, NY 10022
(212) 355-4525

Ed Carpenter
1812 N.W. 24th Ave.
Portland, OR 97210
(503) 224-6729

L. E. Carpenter and Company
170 N. Main St.
Wharton, NJ 07885
(201) 366-2020

Casa Bella Imports
215 E. 58th St.
New York, NY 10022
(212) 688-2020

Casa Bique Ltd.
500 Carolina Ave., P.O. Box 788
Thomasville, NC 27360
(919) 475-9136

Casa Stradivari
200 Lexington Ave.
New York, NY 10016
(212) 684-5990

Castec, Inc.
7531 Coldwater Canyon Blvd.
North Hollywood, CA 91605
(818) 503-8300

Castelli Furniture Inc.
116 Wilbur Pl.
P.O. Box 509
Bohemia, NY 11716
(516) 589-0707

Celia, Inc.
2619 W. Exposition Blvd.
Los Angeles, CA 90018
(213) 734-8746

Robert Chadwick
325 Red Pump Rd.
Nottingham, PA 19362
(215) 932-8637

Chemetal Corp.
132 Water St., P.O. Box 929
Norwalk, CT 06856
(203) 866-5256

Robert Chehayl
49 Harrison St.
Hoboken, NJ 07030
(201) 798-3018

Cherry Creek Enterprises
937 Santa Fe Dr.
Denver, CO 80204
(303) 892-1819

The Children's Room
318 E. 45th St.
New York, NY 10017
(212) 687-3868

China Seas, Inc.
21 E. 4th St.
New York, NY 10003
(212) 420-1170

Michael S. Chinn
Department of Art and Design
158 College of Design
Iowa State University
Ames, IA 50011
(515) 294-6724

CI Designs
574 Boston Ave., P.O. Box 191
Medford, MA 02155
(617) 391-7800

Classic Illumination Inc.
2743 Ninth St.
Berkeley, CA 94710
(415) 849-1842

Classic Moulders
911 N. Railroad Ave.
West Palm Beach, FL 33401
(305) 659-4200

Michael Coffey
River Rd.
West Lebanon, NH 03784
(603) 298-8124

Colonnade Carpets, Collins & Aikman
Corp.
210 Madison Ave.
New York, NY 10016
(212) 578-1217

Mary Rawcliffe Colton
2821 Indiana N.E.
Albuquerque, NM 87110
(505) 881-3944

Conversions
11 Sargent Ave.
Providence, RI 02906
(401) 831-7999

Copperlite Corp.
10 Research Dr.
Stratford, CT 06497
(203) 334-5717

Country Floors, Inc.
300 E. 61st St.
New York, NY 10021
(212) 758-7414

Creative Additions, Ltd.
134 W. 26th St.
New York, NY 10001
(212) 679-1515

David Cress
274 N. Goodman St.
Rochester, NY 14607
(716) 442-9657

Or:

Rosanne Raab Associates
60 Franklin Rd.
Scarsdale, NY 10583
(914) 472-8788

Curvalinear
115 14th Ave. S.
Seattle, WA 98144
(206) 323-5471

Cy Mann Designs
D & D Building
979 Third Ave.
New York, NY 10022
(212) 758-6830

Cyrna International
The Merchandise Mart
Space 12-101
Chicago, IL 60654
(312) 329-0906

Peter Danko & Associates, Inc.
7492-F Old Alexander Ferry Rd.
Clinton, MD 20735
(301) 292-1653

Davis Furniture Industries, Inc.
602 W. Linden St.
P.O. Box 2065
High Point, NC 27261
(919) 889-2009

Davis & Warshow Inc.
57-22 48th St.
Maspeth, NY 11378
(718) 937-9500

Deck House
930 Main St.
Acton, MA 01720
(617) 259-9450

The Decorative Hardware Studio
160 King St.
Chappaqua, NY 10514
(914) 238-5220

Decorators Supply Corp.
3610-12 S. Morgan St., No. 26
Chicago, IL 60609
(312) 847-6300

Deschemaker Fabrics
979 Third Ave.
New York, NY 10022
(212) 319-5730

Designers Tile International
6939 S.W. 57th Ave.
Miami, FL 33143
(305) 661-1581

Devoe & Raynolds Co.
4000 Dupont Circle
Louisville, KY 40207
(502) 897-9861

Directional Furniture Showroom
200 Lexington Ave.
New York, NY 10016
(212) 696-1088

Domus International
5100 Travis St.
Houston, TX 77002
(713) 522-1808

Donghia Furniture
485 Broadway
New York, NY 10013
(212) 925-2777

The Door Store, Inc.
3140 M. St., N.W.
Washington, D.C. 20007
(202) 333-8170

Dovetail, Inc.
750 Suffolk St.
Box 1569-52
Lowell, MA 01853
(617) 454-2944

E. I. DuPont de Nemours & Co., Inc.
Market St., Room X39196
Wilmington, DE 19898
(302) 774-1000

Dunbar
601 S. Fulton St.
Berne, IN 46711
(219) 589-2111

Dux
305 E. 63rd St.
New York, NY 10021
(212) 752-3897

David Ebner
12 Bell St.
Bellport, NY 11713
(516) 286-4523

Eljer Plumbingware
Three Gateway Center
Pittsburgh, PA 15222
(412) 553-7243

Elkay Mfg. Co.
2222 Camden Ct.
Oak Brook, IL 60521
(312) 986-8484

Elliptipar, Inc.
145 Orange Ave.
West Haven, CT 06516
(203) 932-2266

Ello Furniture
1034 Elm St.
Rockford, IL 61101
(815) 964-8601

Elon Inc.
642 Sawmill River Rd.
Ardsley, NY 10502
(914) 693-8000

Entasis
5301 Westband Circle
Bethesda, MD 20816
(703) 525-8478

Ergonom Corporation
13311 Sherman Way
N. Hollywood, CA 91605
(818) 503-0013

East Coast Office:

2500 83rd St., Bldg. 6A
North Bergen, NJ 07047
(914) 967-4284

Erwin-Lambeth Inc.
201 E. Holly Hill Rd.
Thomasville, NC 27360
(919) 476-7751

Eurotex
165 W. Ontario St.
Philadelphia, PA 19140
(215) 739-8844

A.T. Euster Furniture Co.
3300 N.E. Second Ave.
Miami, FL 33137
(305) 573-3200

Fabricut
9303 E. 46th St.
Box 45490
Tulsa, OK 74145
(918) 622-7700

Fabri-Trak, Unique Concepts Inc.
59 Willet St.
Bloomfield, NJ 07003
(201) 532-2393

Falcon Products Inc.
9387 Dielman Industrial Dr.
P.O. Box 21569
St. Louis, MO 63132
(314) 991-9200

Sandra & Richard Farrell
P.O. Box 108
East Killingly, CT 06243
(203) 774-8967

Edward Fields Inc.
232 E. 59th St.
New York, NY 10022
(212) 754-1944

Wayne Filan
Shoreham, VT 05770
(802) 897-2606

Finlandia Fabrics
P.O. Box 185
Exton, PA 19341
(215) 363-2235

First Editions Wallcoverings & Fabrics Inc.
979 Third Ave.
New York, NY 10022
(212) 355-1150

Floordesigns, Inc.
25 Rhode Island St. #218
San Francisco, CA 94103
(415) 626-1005

Focal Point, Inc.
2005 Marietta Rd., N.W.
Atlanta, GA 30318
(404) 351-0820

Forbes Monselle, Inc.
Pacific Design Center
8687 Melrose Ave.
Los Angeles, CA 90069
(213) 652-4242

Formica Corp.
1501 Broadway
New York, NY 10036
(212) 382-2660

Forms & Surfaces
Box 5215
Santa Barbara, CA 93108
(805) 969-7721

Ian Forsberg
2042 Vine St.
Berkeley, CA 94709
(415) 548-4032

The Fräbel Gallery
231 Peachtree St., N.E.
Atlanta, GA 30303
(404) 659-2832

Fresh Impressions Inc.
882 Rt. 22
Somerville, NJ 08876
(201) 526-5353

Functional Office Furniture
1281 Andersen Dr.
San Rafael, CA 94901
(415) 457-4143

James B. Furman Glass Studio
27 W. Main St.
Trumansburg, NY 14886
(607) 387-4141

Furniture of the Twentieth Century, Inc.
227 W. 17th St.
New York, NY 10011
(212) 929-6023

Gaggenau USA Corp.
5 Commonwealth Ave.
Woburn, MA 01801
(617) 938-1655

General Drapery Services, Inc.
635 W. 23rd St.
New York, NY 10011
(212) 924-7200

General Mica Corp.
1850 N.E. 144th St.
N. Miami, FL 33181
(305) 949-7247

GIA International Designs, Inc.
430 E. 59th St.
New York, NY 10022
(212) 753-4255

Anthony Giachetti
Box 504
East Boothbay, ME 04544
(207) 633-3740

Glassmasters Guild
27 W. 23rd St.
New York, NY 10010
(212) 929-7978

Glidden
925 Euclid Ave.
Cleveland, OH 44115
(216) 344-8216

GMT Associates
1255 Oak Point Ave.
Bronx, NY 10474
(212) 991-8500

Jane Goco
794 Scott Rd.
Box 88
Lewisville, NC 27023
(919) 945-3851

Yves Gonnet, Inc.
979 Third Ave.
New York, NY 10022
(212) 758-8220

Gotemobler
1 Westchester Plaza
Elmsford, NY 10523
(914) 592-4812

Ruth Gowell
7010 Aronow Dr.
Falls Church, VA 22042
(703) 532-8645

Greenbaum Collection
101 Washington St.
Paterson, NJ 07505
(201) 279-3000

Greene's Lighting Fixtures, Inc.
1059 Third Ave.
New York, NY 10021
(212) 753-2507

Grohe America Inc.
2677 Coyle Ave.
Elk Grove Village, IL 60007
(312) 640-6650

Groundworks
231 E. 58th St.
New York, NY 10022
(212) 759-8250

P. E. Guerin Inc.
23 Jane St.
New York, NY 10014
(212) 243-5270

Gulistan Carpet by J.P. Stevens & Co., Inc.
P.O. Box A
Aberdeen, NC 28315
(919) 944-2371

Gullan Henley International
Importers of: Bieffe USA
227 W. 17th St.
New York, NY 10011
(212) 741-3384

The Gunlocke Co., Inc.
One Gunlocke Dr.
Wayland, NY 14572
(716) 728-5111

V. Guttman Corp.
Importers of: Algemene Fluweelweverij
95 Madison Ave.
New York, NY 10016
(212) 689-1899

H. & Z. Marbleworks Inc.
179 Summerfield St.
P.O. Box 241
Scarsdale, NY 10583
(914) 472-5666

Habitat International Ltd.
150 E. 58th St.
New York, NY 10022
(212) 758-0926

Dorothy Hafner
44 Cooper Square #3R
New York, NY 10003
(212) 677-9797

Paul Hanson
610 Commercial Ave.
Carlstadt, NJ 07072
(201) 933-4873

Harmony Carpet Corp.
979 Third Ave.
New York, NY 10022
(212) 355-6000

Hastings Tile & Il Bagno Collection
30 Commercial St.
Freeport, NY 11520
(516) 379-3500

Haworth, Inc.
1 Haworth Center
Holland, MI 49423
(810) 292-6154

Heinz & Co.
P.O. Box 663
Oak Park, IL 60303
(312) 383-1310

Henredon Furniture Industries, Inc.
P.O. Box 70
Morganton, NC 28655
(704) 437-5261

Hettich America Corp.
12428 Sam Neely Rd.
P.O. Box 7664
Charlotte, NC 28217
(704) 588-6666

S. M. Hexter Co.
2800 Superior Ave.
Cleveland, OH 44114
(216) 696-0146

Hilo Steiner
507 Broad St.
Shrewsbury, NJ 07701
(201) 741-5862

Hoboken Wood Flooring Corp.
100 Willow St.
Box 510
E. Rutherford, NJ 07073
(201) 933-9700

House of Troy
Box 126
North Troy, VT 05859
(802) 988-2896

Victoria Howe
P.O. Box 66
Cropseyville, NY 12052
(518) 279-9318

Todd Hoyer
139 Higgins Hill
P.O. Box 1451
Bisbee, AZ 85603
(602) 432-4893

Hunter Douglas Inc.
87 Rte. 17 N.
Maywood, NJ 07607
(201) 368-2600

ICF (International Contract Furnishers)
305 E. 63rd St.
New York, NY 10021
(212) 750-0900

ID International
979 Third Ave., #919
New York, NY 10022
(212) 688-3580

IKEA Pennsylvania Inc.
Plymouth Meeting Mall
Plymouth Meeting, PA 19462
(215) 834-0150

Illuminating Experiences, Inc.
107 Trumbull St.
Elizabeth, NJ 07206
(201) 527-8847

Imperial Wallcoverings, Collins & Aikman
  Corp.
23645 Mercantile Rd.
Cleveland, OH 44122
(216) 464-3700

IPI (Innovative Products for Interiors, Inc.)
315 E. 62nd St.
New York, NY 10021
(212) 838-2900

Integra Chairs
Distributed by: Norix Group, Inc.
P.O. Box 298
Batavia, IL 60510-0298
(312) 879-6160

Interface
P.O. Box 1503
Orchard Hill Rd.
LaGrange, GA 30241
(404) 882-1891

Interna Designs, Ltd.
The Merchandise Mart
Space 6-168
Chicago, IL 60654
(312) 467-6076

International Designs & Surfaces
(INDESCO)
330 Nassau Ave.
Brooklyn, NY 11222
(718) 387-8001

Intrends International
Walker & Zanger, Inc.
Box 241
Scarsdale, NY 10583
(914) 472-5666

Irreplaceable Artifacts
14 Second Ave.
New York, NY 10003
(212) 777-2900

Italia Imports, Inc.
61 N.W. 36th St.
Miami, FL 33127
(305) 576-7235

Dakota Jackson Inc.
306 E. 61st St.
New York, NY 10021
(212) 838-9444

Jade Intarsia
Mohawk Oil Canada, Ltd.
6400 Roberts St.
Burnaby, BC V5G 4G2
Canada
(604) 299-7244
USA 1-800-663-8352

Philip Jameson
Sonoma State University
Department of Art
Rohnert Park, CA 94978
(707) 664-2151

Jenn-Air Corp.
3035 Shadeland
Indianapolis, IN 46226
(317) 545-2271

Jensen-Lewis Co., Inc.
89 Seventh Ave.
New York, NY 10011
(212) 929-4880

Jurs Architectural Glass
1681 8th St.
Oakland, CA 94607
(415) 763-6796

Kafra Modern Furniture
via Cavour, 78
22053 Lecco
Italy
(0341) 36.90.68

Vladimir Kagan Designs
232 E. 59th St.
New York, NY 10022
(212) 371-1512

John A. Kapel
80 Skywood Way
Woodside, CA 94062
(415) 851-0888

Karastan Rug Mills
919 Third Ave.
New York, NY 10022
(212) 980-3434

Katzenbach & Warren, Inc.
950 Third Ave.
New York, NY 10022
(212) 759-5410

Jeff Kellar
P.O. Box 4770
Portland, ME 04112
(207) 773-6269

Kenmore Carpet Corp.
979 Third Ave.
New York, NY 11557
(212) 755-8400

Kenmore Industries Inc.
44 Kilby St.
Boston, MA 02109
(617) 523-4008

Michael Kennedy Studios
1927 7th Ave.
Seattle, WA 98101
(206) 441-3737

Kentile Floors Inc.
58 Second Ave.
Brooklyn, NY 11215
(718) 768-9500

Kinetics Furniture
110 Carrier Dr.
Rexdale, ONT M9W 5R1
Canada
(416) 675-4300

Ray King
603 S. 10th St.
Philadelphia, PA 19147
(215) 627-5112

Kirk-Brummel Associates
979 Third Ave.
Suite 503N
New York, NY 10022
(212) 477-8590

Kirsch Co.
309 N. Prospect St.
P.O. Box 0370
Sturgis, MI 49091
(616) 651-0211

Klise Manufacturing Co.
601 Maryland Ave.
Grand Rapids, MI 49505
(616) 459-4283

Knoll International
The Knoll Building
655 Madison Ave.
New York, NY 10021
(212) 826-2400

Koch & Lowy Inc.
21-24 39th Ave.
Long Island City, NY 11101
(718) 786-3520

Kohler Co.
Kohler, WI 53044
(414) 457-4441

George Kovacs Lighting, Inc.
330 E. 59th St.
New York, NY 10022
(212) 838-3400

Krug Inc.
111 Ahrens St. W.
Kitchener ONT N2H 4C2
Canada
(519) 743-8281

LaLune Willow Collection
241 N. Broadway
Milwaukee, WI 53202
(414) 271-1172

Liza Lamb
533 Glenwood Rd.
Binghamton, NY 13905
(607) 770-0159

Lazin Lighting
23 Second Ave.
New York, NY 10003
(212) 473-2236

Lee/Jofa
800 Central Blvd.
Carlstadt, NJ 07072
(201) 438-8444

Lees Carpets
Valley Forge Corporate Center
King of Prussia, PA 19406
(215) 666-7770

Let There Be Neon
P.O. Box 337, Canal St. Station
New York, NY 10013
(212) 966-4772

Bruce Lenore
92 Meridian St.
Providence, RI 02908
(401) 273-9728

Mark S. Levin
914 Thomas St.
Oak Park, IL 60302
(312) 848-5343

Robert Levine
The Works Gallery East
28A Jobs Lane
Southampton, NY 11968
(516) 283-5093

Levolor Lorentzen, Inc.
1280 Wall St. W.
Lyndhurst, NJ 07071
(201) 460-8400

Lighting Associates Inc.
305 E. 63rd St.
New York, NY 10021
(212) 751-0575

Lightolier, Inc.
346 Claremont Ave.
Jersey City, NJ 07305
(201) 333-5120

Lightworks
3345 W. Hunting Park Ave.
Philadelphia, PA 19132
(215) 223-9200

Lithonia Downlighting
Box 195
Vermilion, OH 44089
(216) 967-3131

Tom Loeser
16 Emily St.
Cambridge, MA 02139
(617) 661-9836

Lübke International Design
P.O. Box 4795
High Point, NC 27263
(919) 884-8042

Or in Canada:

c/o Pieter Schat
P.O. Box 202, Stn. M
299 Glenlake Ave.
Toronto, ONT M6S 4T3
Canada
(416) 769-0812

Luxurious Laminates
Pine Island Tpk., P.O. Box 325
Pine Island, NY 10969
(914) 258-4841

Jere Lykins
P.O. Box 580
Mount Berry, GA 30149
(404) 232-5374

Kenneth Lynch & Sons
78 Danbury Rd.
Box 488
Wilton, CT 06897
(203) 762-8363

William Lyons Design Craft, Inc.
41-21 28th St.
Long Island City, NY 11101
(718) 786-0661

Elizabeth MacDonald
Box 205
Bridgewater, CT 06752
(203) 354-0594

Mark McDonnell
12 Rhode Island Ave.
Providence, RI 02906
(401) 331-2958

Louis Mackall & Partner
50 Maple St.
Branford, CT 06405
(203) 488-8364

Robert McKeown
23970 Azevedo Ave.
Haywood, CA 94541
(415) 582-4914

John McNaughton
Indiana State University Evansville
8600 University Blvd.
Evansville, IN 47712
(812) 464-1884

Marrazi USA, Inc.
55 Clay & Scyene Rd.
Sunnyvale, TX 75182
(214) 226-0110

Marble Concepts
400 Northern Blvd.
Great Neck, NY 11021
(516) 487-4679

Marble Technics Ltd.
150 E. 58th St.
New York, NY 10155
(212) 750-9189

John Marcoux
283 George St.
Providence, RI 02906
(401) 351-1398

The Albert Martin Company
131 Oliver St.
Randleman, NC 27317
(919) 498-4101

Maville Interiors
200 Lexington Ave.
New York, NY 10016
(212) 689-3662

Mecho Shade Corp.
42-03 35th St.
Long Island City, NY 11101
(718) 729-2020

Jeff Messerschmidt Designs
P.O. Box 382
Dallas, GA 30132
(404) 942-5949

Metropolitan Lighting Fixture Co., Inc.
1010 Third Ave.
New York, NY 10021
(212) 838-2425

MDI (Meuble Design International, Inc.)
P.O. Box 19188
Washington, D.C. 20036
(202) 293-2905

Herman Miller, Inc.
8500 Bryon Rd.
Zeeland, MI 49464
(616) 772-3300

Howard Miller Clock Co.
860 Main St.
Zeeland, MI 49464
(616) 772-9131

Milliken and Company
201 Industrial Dr.
LaGrange, GA 30241
(404) 883-5511

Miroir Brot, U.S.A.
5555 S. Sepulveda Blvd.
Culver City, CA 90230
(213) 204-4400

Robin Mix
Tunbridge Glassworks
Tunbridge, VT 05077
(802) 889-3430

Modern Age Galleries
795 Broadway
New York, NY 10003
(212) 674-5603

Modern Mode, Inc.
111 San Leandro Blvd.
San Leandro, CA 94577
(415) 568-6650

Mohawk Carpets
1755 The Exchange
Atlanta, GA 30339
(404) 955-4002

Peter Mollica
10033 Broadway Terr.
Oakland, CA 94611
(415) 655-5736

Mondrian, Inc.
1021 Second Ave.
New York, NY 10022
(212) 355-7373

Moser Contract Furniture
P.O. Box 128D
New Gloucester, ME 04260
(207) 926-3233

Murphy Door Bed Co.
40 E. 34th St.
New York, NY 10016-4595
(212) 682-8936

Museum of Modern Art
The Museum Store
11 W. 53rd St.
New York, NY 10019
(212) 708-9888

Mylen Industries
650 Washington St., Box 350
Peekskill, NY 10566
(212) 585-6767

Nanik
7200 Stewart Ave.
Wausau, WI 54401
(715) 842-4653

Natural Vinyl Floor Co., Inc.
4401 Mars Hill Rd.
Box 1302
Florence, AL 35631
(800) 633-3380

Nemschoff Chairs, Inc.
2218 W. Water St.
Sheboygan, WI 53081
(414) 457-7726

Nessen Lamps Inc.
621 E. 216th St.
Bronx, NY 10467
(212) 231-0221

Nienkämper
300 King St. E.
Toronto, ONT
Canada M5V 1J5
(416) 298-5700

E.A. Nord Co., Inc.
300 W. Marine View Dr.
Box 1187
Everett, WA 98206
(206) 259-9292

The October Co., Inc.
51 Ferry St.
Box 71
Easthampton, MA 01027
(413) 527-9380

OJVM Linen Wallcoverings
4B Marlboro Industrial Park
P.O. Box 117
Marlboro, NJ 07746
(201) 780-3202

Origlia USA Inc.
200 Lexington Ave.
New York, NY 10016
(212) 532-0075

Jeanne Otis
The Hand and the Spirit Crafts Gallery
4222 N. Marshall Way
Scottsdale, AZ 85251
(602) 946-4529

The Pace Collection Inc.
11-11 34th Ave.
Long Island City, NY 11106
(718) 721-8201

Palazzetti, Inc.
215 Lexington Ave.
New York, NY 10016
(212) 684-1199

Parma Tile Mosaic & Marble Co., Inc.
1438 Astoria Blvd.
Astoria, NY 11102
(718) 278-3060

Patterson, Flynn & Martin Inc.
950 Third Ave.
New York, NY 10022
(212) 751-6414

Paul Associates, Inc.
42-05 10th St.
Long Island City, NY 11101
(718) 784-2244

Peter Pepper Products, Inc.
17929 S. Susana Rd.
P.O. Box 4758
Compton, CA 90224
(213) 979-0815

Pittsburgh Corning Corp.
800 Presque Isle Dr.
Pittsburgh, PA 15239
(412) 327-6100

Anne Flatin Pixley
The Hand and the Spirit Crafts Gallery
4222 N. Marshall Way
Scottsdale, AZ 85251
(602) 946-4529

Plexability
New York Design Center
Suite 506
200 Lexington Ave.
New York, NY 10016
(212) 679-7826

Plexi-Craft Quality Products Corp.
514 W. 24th St.
New York, NY 10011
(212) 924-3244

Poggenpohl USA Corp.
6 Pearl Court
Allendale, NJ 07401
(201) 934-1511

Potlatch Corporation
Hwy. 79 E.
P.O. Box 916
Stuttgart, AR 72160
(501) 673-1606

The Pottery Barn
175 Clearbrook Rd.
Elmsford, NY 10523
(914) 592-2330

Powell & Tierney Furniture
One Cottage St.
Easthampton, MA 01027
(413) 527-4952

Pratt & Lambert Inc.
75 Tonawanda St.
Buffalo, NY 14207
(716) 873-6000

Princeton Energy Group
575 Ewing St.
Princeton, NJ 08540
(609) 921-1965

Pritam & Eames
29 Race Lane
East Hampton, NY 11937
(516) 324-7111

Progress Lighting
G & Erie Roads
Philadelphia, PA 19134
(215) 289-1200

Puccio/European Marble Works, Inc.
661 Driggs Ave.
Brooklyn, NY 11211
(212) 387-9778

Quatrelle, Inc.
200 Lexington Ave.
New York, NY 10016
(212) 686-6061

Katherine Radcliffe
7 Jane St.
New York, NY 10014
(212) 691-4697

Rambusch
40 W. 13th St.
New York, NY 10011
(212) 675-0400

Beverly Reiser
6979 Exeter Dr.
Oakland, CA 94611
(415) 482-2483

Ron Rezek/Lighting
5522 Venice Blvd.
Los Angeles, CA 90019
(213) 931-2488

Joseph Richter, Inc.
249 E. 57th St.
New York, NY 10022
(212) 755-6094

Rising & Nelson Slate Co., Inc.
West Pawlet, VT 05775
(802) 645-0150

Sheila Ritz
149-151 Grand St.
Brooklyn, NY 11211
(718) 387-3286

Robern, Inc.
1670 Winchester Road
Bensalem, PA 19020
(215) 245-6550

Robinson Iron Corp.
Robinson Rd.
Alexander City, AL 35010
(205) 329-8486

Roche-Bobois
333 N. Wells St.
Chicago, IL 60610
(312) 951-9080

Maya Romanoff Textiles
4722 N. Malden Ave.
Chicago, IL 60640
(312) 271-0388

Rose/Carter, San Francisco
1174 Howard St.
San Francisco, CA 94103
(415) 621-3054

Rosecore Carpet Co., Inc.
979 Third Ave.
New York, NY 10022
(212) 421-7272

Rosecore Handprints
979 Third Ave.
New York, NY 10022
(212) 752-8013

Jon Route
P.O. Box 4823
Overland Park, KS 66204
(913) 648-6099

Rutt Custom Kitchens
Route 23
Goodville, PA 17528
(215) 445-6751

St. Charles Manufacturing Co.
1611 E. Main St.
St. Charles, IL 60174
(312) 584-3800

Hap Sakwa
1330 8th St.
Baywood Park, CA 93402
(805) 528-7585

Saporiti Italia & Campaniello Imports, Ltd.
225 E. 57th St.
New York, NY 10022
(212) 371-3700

Saxony Carpet Co., Inc.
979 Third Ave.
New York, NY 10022
(212) 755-7100

Scalamandré Inc.
950 Third Ave.
New York, NY 10022
(212) 980-3888

Scalia Inc.
305 E. 63rd St.
New York, NY 10021
(212) 759-3943

Scandiline
1217 W. Artesia Blvd.
Compton, CA 90220
(213) 537-6411

Scandinavian Design
127 E. 59th St.
Room 203
New York, NY 10022
(212) 755-6078

Schumacher
939 Third Ave.
New York, NY 10022
(212) 644-5900

Scope Furniture Ltd.
407 W. 13th St.
New York, NY 10014
(212) 243-0488

SieMatic
Pacific Design Center
Suite 446
8687 Melrose Ave.
Los Angeles, CA 90069
(213) 395-8394

Sinclair Paint, Wallcovering, Fabric
2500 S. Atlantic Blvd.
Los Angeles, CA 90040
(213) 268-2511

Smith Metal Arts
1721 Elmwood Ave.
Buffalo, NY 14207
(716) 873-3083

Smolka Co. Inc.
182 Madison Ave.
New York, NY 10016
(212) 679-2700

René Soulard
1833 13th Ave. #208
Seattle, WA 98112
(206) 328-1164

Robert Sperry
120 E. Edgar St.
Seattle, WA 98102
(206) 242-8688

Karl Springer Ltd.
306 E. 61st St.
New York, NY 10021
(212) 752-1695

Starbuck Goldner Studios
315 W. Fourth St.
Bethlehem, PA 18015
(215) 866-6321

Stark Carpet
979 Third Ave.
New York, NY 10022
(212) 752-9000

Stendig, Inc.
410 E. 62nd St.
New York, NY 10021
(212) 838-6050

Sterling Prints
23645 Mercantile Rd.
Cleveland, OH 44122
(216) 464-3700

Subacchi Furniture Inc.
46-24 28th St.
Long Island City, NY 11101
(212) 361-0551

Sunar-Hauserman
5711 Grant Ave.
Cleveland, OH 44105
(216) 883-1400

Sunrise Moulding & Frame Corp.
154 26th St.
Brooklyn, NY 11232
(718) 499-1710

Sun System Solar Greenhouses
60 Vanderbilt Motor Pkwy.
Commack, NY 11725
(516) 543-7600

Taos Clay Products, Inc.
Box 15
Taos, NM 87571
(505) 758-9513

Tarkett
P.O. Box 264
Parsippany, NJ 07054
(201) 428-9000

Janet Taylor
The Hand and the Spirit Crafts Gallery
4222 N. Marshall Way
Scottsdale, AZ 85251
(602) 946-4529

TEC Designs
118-120 Sandford St.
New Brunswick, NJ 08901
(201) 545-7206

Thayer Coggin Inc.
427 South Rd.
Box 5867
High Point, NC 27262
(919) 889-1700

Seth Thomas
520 Guthridge Court
Norcross, GA 30092
(404) 447-0737

Thonet Industries
491 E. Princess St.
P.O. Box 1587
York, PA 17405
(717) 845-6666

Thunder & Light
147 41st St.
Brooklyn, NY 11232
(718) 499-3777

Marjorie Tomchuk
44 Horton Lane
New Canaan, CT 06840
(203) 972-0137

Trakliting Inc.
14625 E. Clark Ave.
City of Industry, CA 91746
(213) 330-3106

Tromploy
400 Lafayette
New York, NY 10003
(212) 420-1639

Bob Trotman
Rt. 1, Box 100-A2
Casar, NC 28020
(704) 538-8236

U.S. Bells/Robert Fisher
Prospect Harbor, ME 04469
(207) 963-7184

United Wallcoverings, Collins & Aikman Corp.
P.O. Box 22087
Cleveland, OH 44122
(216) 464-3700

Unique Form Originals, Inc.
545 W. 26th St.
Hialeah, FL 33010
(305) 885-1886

Vermont Floors and Woodworking
683 Pine St.
Burlington, VT 05401
(800) 343-8787

Vermont Marble Co.
61 Main St.
Proctor, VT 05765
(802) 459-3311

Verosol USA, Inc.
224 Park West Dr.
RIDC Park West
Pittsburgh, PA 15275
(412) 787-9810

Villeroy & Boch (USA) Inc.
Interstate 80 at New Maple Ave.
Pine Brook, NJ 07058
(201) 575-0550

V'soske Shops, Inc.
155 E. 56th St.
New York, NY 10022
(212) 688-1150

Sherle Wagner International
60 E. 57th St.
New York, NY 10022
(212) 758-3300

Walker & Zanger Inc.
179 Summerfield St.
Box 241
Scarsdale, NY 10583
(914) 472-5666

Wall • Goldfinger Design Associates
7 Belknap St.
Northfield, VT 05663
(802) 485-6261

Wasley Lighting Inc.
Plains Rd.
Essex, CT 06426
(203) 767-0191

Watercolors Inc.
S. Mountain Pass
Garrison, NY 10524
(914) 424-3327

Waterworks
179 South St.
Boston, MA 02111
(617) 482-8811

Judith Weber
50 Webster Ave.
New Rochelle, NY 10801
(914) 235-9027

Wesco Fabrics Inc.
4001 Forest St.
Denver, CO 80216
(303) 388-4101

Tom Wessells
4 Graham Dr.
Newport News, VA 23606
(804) 599-5615

Westchester Marble & Granite, Inc.
179 Summerfield St.
P.O. Box 241
Scarsdale, NY 10583
(914) 472-5666

Western Arts & Tables
91621 Worldway Station
Los Angeles, CA 90009
(213) 978-4966

Westgate Fabrics, Inc.
1000 Fountain Pkwy.
Grand Prairie, TX 75050
(214) 647-2323

Westnofa USA, Inc.
7040 N. Austin Ave.
Niles, IL 60648
(312) 647-7415

Whitehead Studios
The Merchandise Mart
Suite 1234-A
Chicago, IL 60654
(312) 661-1494

Willow and Reed
32-34 111th St.
East Elmhurst, NY 11369
(718) 335-0807

Wilsonart
600 General Bruce Dr.
Temple, TX 76501
(817) 778-2711

Wood-Metal Industries, Inc.
Wood-Mode Cabinetry
Kreamer, PA 17833
(717) 374-2711

Woodson Fabrics
979 Third Ave.
New York, NY 10016
(212) 684-0330

Workbench Contract
470 Park Ave. S.
New York, NY 10016
(212) 532-7900

The Wrecking Bar, Inc.
2601 McKinney Ave.
Dallas, TX 75204
(214) 826-1717

Rick Wrigley
80 Race St.
Holyoke, MA 01040
(413) 536-2034

Or

ZONA
484 Broome St.
New York, NY 10013
(212) 925-6750

York Spiral Stair
Rt. 32
N. Vassalboro, ME 04962
(207) 872-5558

Biblio-
graphy

Almeida, Philip. *How to Decorate a Dump.* Secaucus, N.J.: Lyle Stuart, 1983.

Banham, Rayner. *Theory and Design in the First Machine Age.* Cambridge, Mass.: MIT Press, 1980.

Beard, Geoffrey. *International Modern Glass.* New York: Charles Scribner's Sons, 1978.

Beer, Eileene Harrison. *Scandinavian Design: Objects of a Life Style.* New York: The American-Scandinavian Foundation/Farrar, Straus & Giroux, 1975.

Birks, Tony. *Art of the Modern Potter.* New York: Van Nostrand Reinhold Co., 1976.

Clark, Garth R. and Margie Hughto. *A Century of Ceramics in the United States,* 1879-1979. New York: E. P. Dutton & Co., 1979.

Conran, Terence. *The Bed and Bath Book.* New York: Crown Publishers, 1978.

_____. *The House Book.* New York: Crown Publishers, 1976.

_____. *The Kitchen Book.* New York: Crown Publishers, 1977.

Designers Guild. *Soft Furnishings: Ideas and Fabrics by Designers.* New York: Farrar, Straus & Giroux, 1980.

Gablik, Suzi. *Progress in Art.* New York: Rizzoli International Publications, 1977.

Garner, Philippe. *Contemporary Decorative Arts.* New York: Facts on File, Inc., 1980.

_____. *The Encyclopedia of Decorative Arts,* 1890-1940. New York: Van Nostrand Reinhold Co., 1979.

Greif, Martin. *Depression Modern: The Thirties Style in America.* New York: Universe Books, 1975.

Jencks, Charles. *The Language of Post-Modern Architecture.* New York: Rizzoli International Publications, 1980.

_____. *Late-Modern Architecture.* New York: Rizzoli International Publications, 1980.

_____. *Le Corbusier and the Tragic View of Architecture.* Cambridge, Mass.: Harvard University Press, 1974.

_____. *Post-Modern Classicism: The New Synthesis.* New York: Rizzoli International Publications, 1980.

Joel, David. *Furniture Design Set Free.* London, 1969.

Johnson, Philip C. *Mies van der Rohe.* Boston: Museum of Modern Art/New York Graphic Society, 1978.

Kron, Joan and Suzanne Slesin. *High-Tech: The Industrial Source Book for the Home.* New York: Clarkson N. Potter, 1978.

McIlhany, Sterling. *Art as Design: Design as Art.* New York: Van Nostrand Reinhold Co., 1970.

Meadmore, Clement. *The Modern Chair: Classics in Production.* New York: Van Nostrand Reinhold Co., 1979.

Stennett-Wilson, Ronald. *Modern Glass.* New York: Van Nostrand Reinhold Co., 1975.

Stewart, Richard. *Modern Design in Metal.* Central Islip, N.Y.: Transatlantic Arts, Inc., 1979.

Venturi, Robert. *Learning from Las Vegas.* Cambridge, Mass.: MIT Press, 1977.

Index